Computer Connection Mysteries Solved

Graham Wideman with
Michael Kern

Howard W. Sams & Co.
A Division of Macmillan, Inc.
4300 West 62nd Street, Indianapolis, IN 46268 USA

To Jasmin and all my friends.

Pictorial Sketches: *Michael Kern*
Technical Illustration: *Wm. D. Basham*
Companion "Port Buddy" Software: *William Morris*
Inspirations: *Jasmin Wideman and Peter Ross*

Trademarks

Many companies and products are mentioned in this book. In general, most company names are trademarks, and many of these are registered trademarks. The ownership of each of these trademarks is generally by the named company. Many of the product names are also trademarks, some of which may be registered. The author has made an effort to associate the name of the producing company with the mentioned products.

The following list provides information on any product or name ownership:

CP/M: Digital Research Inc.
DEC: Digital Equipment Corporation
Diablo: Xerox Corporation
HP: Hewlett-Packard Company
IBM: International Business Machines Corp.
IDS: Integral Data Systems Inc.
Kaypro: Non Linear Systems Inc.
Lotus 1-2-3: Lotus Development Corp.
Macintosh: Licensed to Apple Computer Inc. by McIntosh Laboratory Inc. MSDOS, Microsoft BASIC: Microsoft Corp.
WordStar: Micropro International
RCA: Radio Corporation of America

FIRST EDITION
FIRST PRINTING—1986

International Standard Book Number: 0-672-22526-3
Library of Congress Catalog Card Number: 86-61397

Electronic Book Publishing Services: *The Publisher's Network, Morrisville, PA*

Printed in the United States of America.

Contents

1

Introduction

This book is all about connecting computer gear and getting it working properly. It is written for the kind of person who wants or needs to know what's going on. Whether you work with computers, you've got a connection problem "nobody" can solve, or you just want to save some time and money on a cable, this book is for you!

Although you will find some of the most comprehensive information available on these subjects, the coverage is *not* overly technical. If a trial-and-error technique is efficient, then I recommend it! On the other hand, if you can use electronics expertise to advantage, I'll show you what you need to know.

Ostensibly then, this book is about a number of topics relating to interfacing a computer to other equipment or to custom-built gadgetry. It's also about principles, opinions, self-reliance, confidence and encouragement; in fact, perhaps these are the *main* subjects of the book.

Principles are very important in this book. Some books attempt to provide specific details on as many specific cases as possible. My opinion is that these attempts are misleadingly inadequate because they have only a very slim chance of being absolutely complete. In addition, they are almost immediately obsolete for current equipment.

Consequently, my choice is to provide principles and techniques by which you can interact with the problems and use your mind to puzzle out a solution. These principles and techniques are not foiled by new equipment, nor by accidental omissions on the part of the author.

So, although I do refer to IBM PCs, Macintoshes, Ataris, Kaypros and so on, I do so only as examples, *not* in an attempt to provide complete information for all machines.

This book is about opinions. The electronics and computer business is not as fact-based as it might intrinsically seem to be. Certainly, correct technical information pertaining to your task exists *somewhere*. However, in many cases you are not going to get to it; it may never even be published. So, part of working in this field concerns nebulous activities, like acquiring a feel for "the way things happen," and knowing which of the available information sources to bet on and work from. You end up playing psychological games like guessing the competence or biases of the writers of technical documents, or the motivations of salespeople.

I don't have access to all of the information either. Therefore, some of what I write in this book is my opinion. When I write "in most situations. . .," I have not done a survey. By the time a survey could be done, it would be too late to be useful. My perspective is not "all knowing." Take my word with as many grains of salt as anyone else's, until you find that what I say makes sense, or actually works in practice.

The book is about self-reliance because ultimately you have to rely on yourself. You either have to rely on yourself or your choice of people to fix your problems. That being the case, this book can provide some information on the problems either to help you do the job or to help you converse with those who are doing the job for you.

I hope to contribute to your confidence in working with the physical aspect of your computer, and the enthusiasm born of the knowledge that you can conquer many of the computer needs which other computer users fear are untouchable mysteries. A part of this attitude is the ability to maintain a good-natured, but healthy (and scientific!) skepticism. Reflections on wry humor are posted at intervals to brighten things up along the way.

Subjects Covered

Here are the main subject areas of this book:

Philosophies and Attitude Alignment: You would be best armed by having some background in the principles of the under-the-hood operation of computers. Chapter 2 gets you going with some "Conversational Electronics"— guaranteed low-math. This is followed by a strict warning about technical documentation, and thoughts on how to interpret dubious details (Chapter 3).

RS-232 Serial: RS232 is a supposed convention used for connecting terminals, modems, computers, printers, plotters, mice and many other devices. This is covered in Chapters 4 through 11.

Centronics Parallel: Chapter 12 covers a convention used chiefly for connecting printers to computers, but also used for some plotters and other devices.

Video: Chapters 13 to 15 give us a look at the variety of conventions in use for attaching video monitors to computer systems.

Power Connections: Chapters 16 and 17 are all about the electric power your computer uses, and the troubles for which it is frequently blamed.

MIDI: (Musical Instrument Digital Interface) An up-and-coming new opportunity for making loud noises with your computer is discussed in Chapter 18.

Disk Drives: Not as frequently plugged or unplugged as other items, but nonetheless deserving of the attention given in Chapter 19.

Miscellaneous Connections: An assortment of input and output devices are covered in Chapter 20.

Custom Connections: For the adventurous but cheap, Chapter 21 offers some opportunities to connect the real world to your computer.

Warning!

In various places throughout this book you will find cautions about things you should or should not do to avoid damage to yourself or your equipment. Since it is best to be extra safe, a few extra warnings can be presented at this time.

Stay Alive!   The signals and signal wiring which are involved in the interfaces in this book are not dangerous to your person. The voltages are low and will do your body no harm, and the ability to deliver current is limited. In addition, there are few procedures which require you to have your computer or other equipment open and switched on.

However, you may have occasion to open up your computer, terminal or other equipment (perhaps to flip switches), which may expose you to either power line voltages, or worse, to the very high voltages which are used to run the picture tube. Equipment varies widely as to how well you are protected from accidents once the cover is removed.

Definitely try to have the power cord disconnected when nosing around inside equipment. But if the equipment contains a picture tube, be aware that the picture tube can store a mighty wallop for perhaps *hours* after being switched off (although newer equipment should take much less time to discharge).

If it is necessary to have the equipment operating while it is open, then do so only with full knowledge of where high voltages might be lurking. It is useful to adopt the old TV-serviceman's custom of wearing rubber-soled shoes, and keeping one hand in a pocket while using only the other hand to poke around with an oscilloscope, meter, or insulated adjustment screwdriver.

The idea is to avoid providing a conductive path for the electricity if the one hand should accidentally contact a dangerous voltage. Using two hands invites disaster, since the conducting path might easily be straight across the chest, near the heart.

Keep Your Equipment Healthy!   It is tempting to believe that if two connectors fit together, then it's OK to go ahead and try to connect them. In fact, even if the cabling is not right, you will often escape with no damage to the equipment. However, don't be lulled into a false sense of security by this. There are many instances where plugging a cable carrying signals of one type into a socket expecting signals of a different type will damage equipment at one or both ends of the cable! Needless to say, this could make for an expensive repair job.

A particularly deceptive, yet common, example is concerned with the use of DB-25 connectors on the IBM PC and compatibles. Normally, the "D"-shaped, 25-pin connector is used for RS-232 hookups. On the PC's back panel, the male DB-25 (with pins) is indeed used for that purpose. However, the female connector (with holes) is used to hook up a Centronics interface printer. If you want to hook up some piece of RS-232 gear, and arrive with some arbitrary RS-232 cable, there's a 50% chance that the cable will have a male plug, and you'll be tempted to plug it into the Centronics port on the PC! This will almost certainly cause distress for you and your computer.

The moral of the story is: read about the type of hookup you want to perform before diving straight in!

2

Some Philosophies of Electronics and Signals

Because this book is about connecting equipment together, it is also about the signals which these machines use to send their "messages." For this reason, I am explaining first a little about signals and electronics. This is by no means a complete course in electronics: it is just enough to allow you to see the general principles involved. Many of you will not need such a basic explanation, but you might skim over it anyway, to see if there is anything new.

For readers who need this explanation, I hope you will find it a painless introduction. It is *not* merely an abbreviated, half-effort thrown in to justify later, more technical discussions. It is an honest attempt to demonstrate the way in which electricity is used in a computer, and to show how it is observed and understood by those of us who work with it.

Perhaps it will even encourage some to go further in their studies of electronics. Remember, electricity is not nearly as difficult or complicated to understand as most books make it seem. It just seems mysterious at first because you can't see it with your own eyes. In fact, for those of us who work with electronics, a top priority is acquiring or devising equipment which will let us "see" what that mischievous electricity is doing! So we do, in fact, think about electricity's behavior as though it is something mechanical and visible.

Inside Your Computer...

If you peek inside your computer, you will see that it consists mainly of thin boards covered with hoards of small, multilegged, rectangular black objects (Figure 2-1). The black objects are called *integrated circuits*, (*ICs* or *chips*) and each of the legs is a connection to circuitry inside the chip. The boards are called *printed circuit*

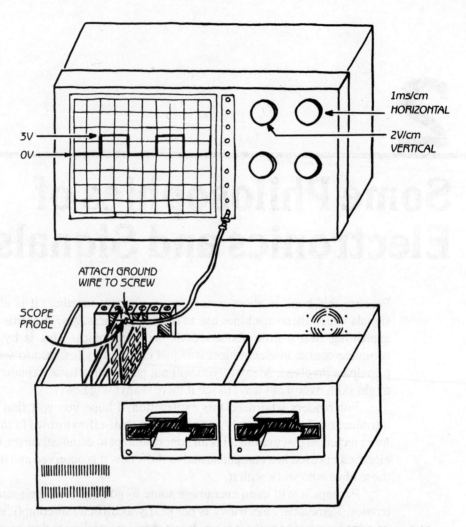

3V

0V

1ms/cm
HORIZONTAL

2V/cm
VERTICAL

ATTACH GROUND
WIRE TO SCREW

SCOPE
PROBE

Figure 2-1 An oscilloscope observes the "conversation" between one IC and its neighbor. The horizontal axis on the scope is time, while the vertical axis is voltage. The conversation shown was first "low," then "high," then "low" . . . and so on.

boards, because upon the boards are printed copper lines, called *traces*. These traces are the wiring which connects the chips to one another. (They don't look copper-colored because the copper is coated with solder, which is silver-colored.)

The computer works because all of these chips can talk to neighboring chips. Each chip carries out some function of the computer's operation, and under control of appropriate software, the whole complicated mass of IC's does something useful, like word processing. What we are interested in is how these chips talk to each other. Not the theory of how they work, but the conventions they use for talking and understanding each other, or indeed, for talking to chips in other equipment like printers and other computers.

"Representation"

To digress for a moment, a concept which is central to computers and electronics is the idea of "representation" of information. Electronics is not exciting or useful simply because we can do all kinds of fancy things with electrons. What makes it exciting is that we can represent information in terms of electrical activity. We can then play with the electrical activity in ways analogous to "thinking," or use it for "transporting" information over distances, then "unrepresent" the electrical activity back into some form of information we can understand.

Such electrical activity, representing information, is called a *signal*.

It is important to understand the representation idea, because it helps to relate something you already understand, the information, to the subjects we will be examining. These subjects include the signals which represent that information in RS-232, Centronics, video interfaces, MIDI, disk drives, and so on.

The pocket calculator provides a very clear example of this. When you push on the keys you are "representing" information (numbers and operations to you) using electrical means (closing a switch under the key to cause some electrical activity). Inside the calculator, these electrical actions set off a chain of electrical events cleverly designed to imitate arithmetic. The result is that certain digits are displayed on the calculator readout; electrical activity representing numbers is converted to a form which we can read.

Similarly, inside a computer, information is represented by electrical activity as it is passed from chip to chip. However, the correspondence between that electrical activity and the information we understand is not immediately clear. This is because there are actually several *layers* of representation occurring.

Voltage, Meters, and Oscilloscopes

It seem logical to start unravelling the computer representation mystery at the bottom layer, and work up to the information layer. Let's start by examining the "conversation" that may be going on between two chips. This conversation is carried out in *voltages*.

Voltage is an electrical characteristic. It could be explained in very complicated terms, but suffice it to say that it is merely a characteristic which can be observed by using a voltmeter, or better yet by using an *oscilloscope*. And guess what—it's measured in units of volts! A voltmeter is capable of giving a readout of voltage on a particular wire, and may have a needle-type indicator or a numeric readout. A small AA or D sized battery, for example, measures 1.5 volts, while the common rectangular "transistor" battery measures 9 volts.

Unfortunately, for our purposes, a voltmeter is not very useful because the voltages on the wires inside a computer change very frequently, perhaps many times per microsecond (one millionth of a second)! So the instrument which is often used is the oscilloscope, which gives a graphical picture of the voltage on a screen. Figure 2-1 shows an oscilloscope displaying a picture of the voltage activity on some wire inside the computer.

The immediately interesting thing to note on the oscilloscope display is that the chips appear to have a very consistent standard for their conversation. The voltages are either about zero, or about 3 volts. These voltages are referred to as "low" and "high." This is one of the conventions of the electronics industry.

High-low operation is described as *digital-logic*. Of course, a mere low or high does not convey much information to us, but the computer designers arranged things so that the high or low output of one chip has some significant meaning to the input of the next chip. Although this high-low conversation may seem rather simple-minded, it turns out that the chips can be made to operate extremely fast and accurately, which results in a computer system of useful intelligence. (In fact, limitation to high-low type operation is what permits accuracy and speed at an inexpensive price. A typical small IC costs less than a dollar, and even the largest are perhaps $10 or $20).

Digression on Logic Families

I've already sneaked in one level of representation here, referring to two specific voltages as "high" and "low." Different chips actually use different voltage ranges for high and low, yet the ideas we are about to discuss are relevant for all chips of the digital-logic variety.

There are a number of different logic families you will hear about from time to time. The oldest types are *DTL* and *RTL*, standing for *Diode Transistor Logic* and *Resistor Transistor Logic*. These types are long obsolete. Following those came *TTL*, which stands for *Transistor Transistor Logic*. This is the "founding family" of the chips used in almost all personal computers. From this family comes the particular selection of voltage ranges for "high" and "low" which are used so widely. This family includes a wide variety of different chips providing functions from simple logic gates to counters, and chips which select which paths data will follow. Most TTL chips have part numbers beginning with a 74, like 74367.

Microprocessors and their large support chips, and also memory chips are not built using TTL technology, yet they are still made to agree with TTL logic voltage levels. Newer versions of TTL have sprung up, the most successful being *Low power Schottky* (LSTTL), which is almost universally used in personal computers because of its higher speed but lower power consumption. LSTTL can handle conversations which flip between high and low at rates up to 80 million transitions per second! LSTTL parts have numbers which start with 74LS, like 74LS645.

These and other logic families will be discussed in further detail a little later.

The Ground Wire

Another word about voltage is in order here. Voltage, in fact, is a relative measurement, just like height. When we say that a mountain is 5000 feet high, we give the measurement as relative to sea-level. Of course, we could measure the height with respect to something else, but we rarely do.

Similarly, in electronics, we glibly speak of the voltage at a certain location being zero or 3 volts or 5 volts. The measurement is with respect to what is called "ground" or "earth." Both of these names have the unfortunate connotation that they refer to the stuff we walk on, which is only occasionally true. *Ground* is simply a wire which runs all around inside the computer providing every chip with a reference against which to interpret the incoming signals, and relative to which to produce output signals.

It is because voltage is relative that voltmeters and oscilloscopes have two input wires. Generally, we hook the one marked "ground" or "negative" onto the ground of the equipment being observed (in this case the computer), and use the "signal" or "positive" probe to hook on to the signal of interest. In this way, the meter or oscilloscope knows that the observed voltage is referenced to ground. Voltmeters and oscilloscopes can also be used to measure the voltage between two non-ground points, but for our purposes this is not terribly useful.

Chips Need Power, Too

Just as a flashlight needs power to operate, so do chips. Also, just as in a flashlight, where the two ends of the battery are connected to the two terminals on the lamp to form a "circuit," so it is with chips. There are power wires running around inside a computer supplying power to all the chips. To economize, one of those power wires is also the ground wire we have just been discussing. Figure 2-2 summarizes this situation.

Back to Representation: Bits and Bytes

How about word-processing? With 256 codes we can use bytes to represent the alphabet, plus numbers and punctuation. Remember the old "secret" code in school: A is 1, B is 2, C is 3, and 3-1-20 spells CAT? Based on the same idea, the code almost everybody uses is called the American Standard Code for Information Interchange, or ASCII, a listing of which is provided in the appendices.

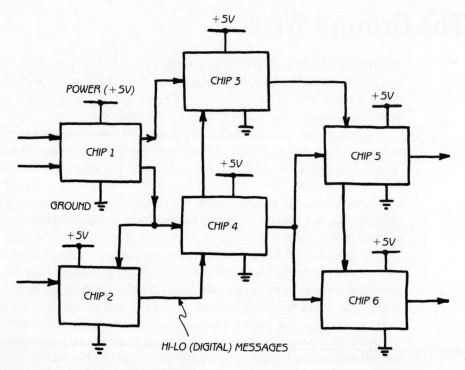

Figure 2-2 A diagram of a computer showing the ground which provides both a power connection and a signal reference voltage.

Bits are still not very useful, because simple ones and zeroes don't relate very well to our everyday lives. The next step is to team up the computer's components in gangs of eight (or more): the memory slots are eight bits wide, the central-processor is eight bits wide and so on. So now information is flowing around eight bits at a time, and these eight-bit groups are called bytes.

If you've had any base-two mathematics, you realize that with 8 bits you can count from 0 to 255 (because there are 256 different combinations of highs and lows which can be made with 8 bits). This would almost be useful if we counted that way, but we don't, so we have some smart people figure out computer languages which can talk to us in normal base-10, and talk to the computer in bytes.

How about word-processing? With 256 codes we can use bytes to represent the alphabet, plus numbers and punctuation. Remember the old "secret" code in school: A is 1, B is 2, C is 3, and 3-1-20 spells CAT? Based on the same idea, the code almost everybody uses is called the American Standard Code for Information Interchange, or ASCII, a listing of which is provided in the appendix.

Now What?

Now we face the decades-old problem of what to do with a bunch of codes knocking around inside a computer. And the decades-old answer is: "Send them somewhere else!". To a modem, a printer, a video screen, another computer, anywhere! Which will take us on to the topics of the rest of this book, namely "How?"

Summary So Far

We have examined how electricity, more specifically voltage, is used to represent information. We are now prepared to look at how certain specific representation schemes work in the communications between equipment involving the various interfaces and conventions covered in this book.

For some of the topics it is helpful to know a little more about how electricity works. If you are eager to get on to some other section of the book, then skip this section until you feel you need it. Otherwise, let's continue.

More About Electricity

I've just introduced you to how voltages are observed in a computer, and how they are used to carry information around, *without* discussing very much about how electricity behaves. The idea was to get you interested in voltages and electricity in general without forcing you to wade through a pile of boring theory. The description was reasonably complete, because we were dealing with a machine that was already built, and where some of the details of electricity had already been taken care of for us.

But in some parts of this book it will be helpful to know a little more, since we are going to be dealing with electrical signals that have been brought outside the computer. We are going to be taking some responsibility for where those signals go, and we're going to be doing some slightly fancy testing.

One of the concepts that is useful to understand is how "strong" a signal is. Inside the computer, the signals are "strong enough" for the inputs that they go to, so we are not concerned. Outside the computer, we may have problems with the strength of the signal, or we may find that knowing the strength helps us test for the signal.

So, on to a few more details.

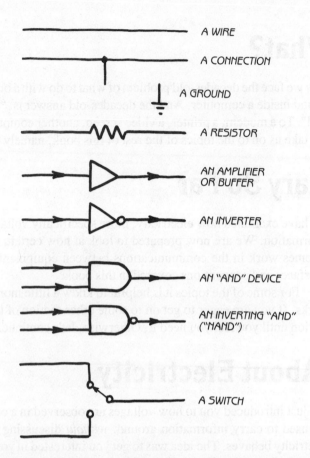

	A WIRE
	A CONNECTION
	A GROUND
	A RESISTOR
	AN AMPLIFIER OR BUFFER
	AN INVERTER
	AN "AND" DEVICE
	AN INVERTING "AND" ("NAND")
	A SWITCH

Figure 2-3   A selection of some of the simpler symbols used in circuit diagrams. The arrows shown on some of the symbols are simply to indicate input or output and are not customarily used.

Digression on Symbols

To discuss some details of electricity and electronics, it will be most convenient to draw diagrams. Most fields of endeavor use some form of diagrams: for example, in the construction of buildings drawings are prepared which show how to assemble the various posts, beams, studs, joists and so on. We might call these "physical" or "pictorial" diagrams, since they are essentially what you would see with your own eyes.

In electronics, the physical appearance of individual components is not terribly important, and the connections may be so convoluted as to be very confusing if diagrammed pictorially. Consequently, a scheme of drawing electronics and electrical diagrams has evolved which represents the components with symbols which clearly shows the type of component, and also shows how the components are connected together. This type of diagram more clearly reveals how the entire assemblage operates.

There are actually some different drawing "languages." The style and symbols used for electrical wiring of a building is partly pictorial, as is that used for automotive wiring. We will be looking at the style used in electronics, which is non-pictorial, but concentrates more on the interconnections and communication.

In the diagrams used here, the symbols are very simple. Wires are indicated by lines, and Figure 2-3 shows some of the other symbols you might see. A dot is sometimes used to indicate a connection, particularly where there might be some ambiguity as to whether intersecting lines (wires) connect or simply cross on the diagram. I will not make an extensive effort to provide all of the possible symbols immediately. Instead I'll introduce other symbols as they are needed.

An Analogy

I am going to introduce an analogy: "Electricity in wires is like pressurized gas in pipes". This is similar to, but slightly better than the more traditional "electricity is like water in pipes." There are, however, several problems with these analogies:

- Electricity is only somewhat like gas or water in pipes. For example, if you get a hole in a pipe the contents leak out, yet you can't get electricity to just pour out of the end of a wire.

- In electronics, there are lots of components joined by wires, while in a plumbing system there are mostly just pipes.

- In electronics we are interested in the use of electricity for "thinking" purposes. Except for certain large white porcelain fixtures in small rooms, plumbing is generally not used for thinking, but merely for supplying water or gas.

- (Most people don't know a whole lot about water or gas anyway. Readers familiar with hydraulics or pneumatics may, however, see some parallels.)

The analogy will, however, serve to get us started. Here are its components:

1. The "substance" of electricity is a "material" called *charge*, which can flow only along *conductors* such as wires. Ignore everything you may have heard about electrons at this stage, we are dealing with charge at a macroscopic level, as though it is a homogeneous substance. In fact, charge is talked about comparatively little in electronics, for the main reason that it is awkward to observe directly. In any case, because we are mostly interested in information, which requires fluctuations, we are more interested in how charge flows around in our pipe-wires.

    By the way, charge is measured in units called *coulombs*, which for electronics purposes are quite big.

2. Voltage is the "pressure" which pushes or pulls the charge around. Just as we can measure the pressure at different locations in a plumbing system, so we can measure voltage at different points in a circuit. In both systems, voltage/pressure difference is a measure of how "eagerly" the charge/gas at a higher-pressure location would like to flow to a lower-pressure location, if a path was provided. Figure 2-4 shows this.

Our restriction that voltage is "relative" is merely the same as restricting pressure measurements to looking at the *difference in pressure* between two parts of the plumbing system.

Unlike gas or water systems, voltage can be negative. Of course, pressure being relative, you sometimes do hear about "negative pressure." However, the pressure can never be less than a vacuum, whereas voltage has no negative limit. It is thus better to conceive of voltage as being a measure of "desire to flow" between two locations.

3. "Current" is the other big word in electricity. It means the *rate of flow* of charge. It is measured in units of *amps*, (amperes) where one amp is one coulomb-per-second. (An amp is quite big for electronics, we generally talk in milliamps [mA] or microamps [µA], which are 1/1,000 and 1/1,000,000 amp respectively).

Current is a very useful concept, partially because it is easy to observe. It can be measured with an *ammeter*. To measure the flow rate in a pipe, you would break the pipe and insert a flowmeter, which would measure gallons or litres per hour. Similarly, to measure the flow in a wire, you break the wire, and insert an ammeter, which measures in amps. Since an amp is quite large for electronics work, we will be dealing in 1/1000 amp (milliamps [mA]).

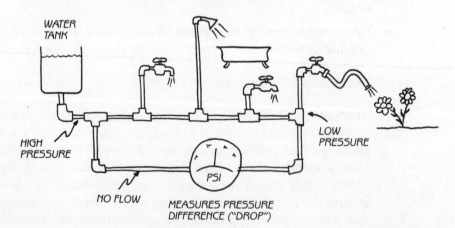

Figure 2-4   A water-in-pipes system, somewhat similar to electricity in wires. Water "wants" to flow from a high-pressure location to a low-pressure location. A pressure gage allows us to measure a pressure difference.

Note: it is common practice to talk about "current flow." This is rather a misnomer, since what is conceptually more correct is "charge flow." "Current" is synonymous with "rate of charge flow."

If a conducting path is available in a circuit between two locations which are of different voltage, then charge will flow from the more positive point to the more negative—from the higher pressure to the lower. Inserting an ammeter would permit measurement of the rate of flow.

4. What stops all of the available charge at one location from immediately rushing to another location when a conducting path is provided? This is done by a characteristic called *resistance*. A simple example is that of a battery powering a light bulb. Figures 2-5 and 2-6 demonstrate these ideas.

Although in electronics wires are usually treated as *ideal conductors* (having zero resistance), a light bulb is not. Hence it presents a restriction to the current from positive to negative end of the battery, in much the same way as would a constriction in a pipe. This resistance is measured in units called *ohms*, where one ohm means that one volt of "pressure difference" will push charge at a rate of one amp (one coulomb per second). The higher the voltage, the higher the resulting current, and the higher the resistance the lower the current.

For electronics, ohms are too small, and most resistances are in hundreds of ohms, or in thousands (kilohm, kohm) or millions of ohms (Megohm, Mohm).

Returning to our light bulb, suppose that the bulb has a resistance of 30 ohms, and the battery has a voltage of 3 volts. A quick calculation shows that the resulting current will be 100 mA. Actually, the resistance of a light bulb increases sharply as

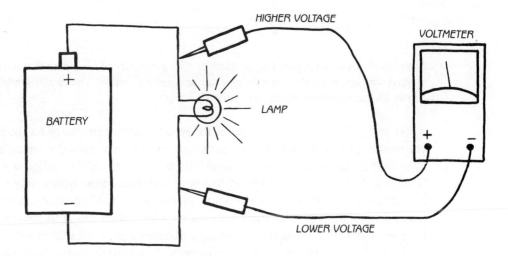

Figure 2-5   A battery powering a lamp. Here a voltmeter would tell us that the voltage across the lamp is simply that of the battery.

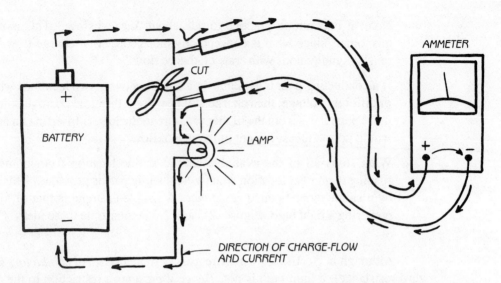

Figure 2-6   Here is the same circuit, with an ammeter reporting the current in the circuit. The current is limited by the resistance of the lamp. Note that according to convention charge flows from positive (bigger charge) to negative (lesser charge), so the direction of current is likewise.

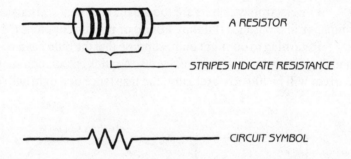

Figure 2-7   A resistor generally looks like a long cylindrical blob with two wires. It is painted with colored stripes which indicate the resistance value. The circuit symbol looks like an awkward path to "resist" the current.

it gets hot, so if you actually measured the resistance with an ohmmeter (bulb cold) you would surmise that it draws much more current than it really does in operation.

One component that is frequently used in electronics is called a *resistor* (Figure 2-7). This is a small cylindrical blob with two wires, whose only job is to provide resistance in a measured amount. Actually, it would be more correct to say that resistors are generally used in positions where their job is to provide some precise influence over current or voltage. Resistors are available in values from fractions of an ohm to hundreds of megohms and are marked with colored stripes to indicate their value.

While current through a light bulb gives off light and heat, a resistor gives off only heat. In electronics-sized quantities there is not much heat, but nonetheless there is some. Resistors are available in different physical sizes for applications where they may need to dissipate more heat. The rate of energy being converted to heat (power) is measured in watts, where:

Power (in watts) = Volts × Amps.

Typical, small electronics resistors are rated at around 0.1 watt, which is to say that with a voltage and current combination up to 0.1W, the resistor will stay reasonably cool.

Ohm's Law and Voltage Dividers

By the way, a couple of paragraphs back I sneaked in *Ohm's Law*, which is merely the observation that in a circuit like Figures 2-8 and 2-9:

Current [amps] = Voltage [volts] / Resistance [ohms]

Of course the current is the current through the resistor, and the voltage is the voltage measured *across* the resistor. Note that the equation still holds nicely if we use units of milliamps with kilohms.

Another useful observation can be made if we transpose the equation. If we know the current and the resistance, we can find the voltage:

Voltage across resistor = Current × Resistance

Suppose we have the arrangement shown in Figure 2-10, a 10-volt battery (yes, I know batteries don't come in that denomination) connected to two resistors, each with a resistance of 1k ohm. If it's 10 volts at the top of the resistors, and zero volts at the bottom, what is it in the middle?

There are a couple of things that boring electronics books tell you about circuits like this one:

1. The total resistance of resistor A in series with resistor B is the sum of the resistances. Pretty obvious?

2. The charge flowing through resistor A is the same as the charge flowing through resistor B because there's nowhere else for it to go. Also obvious? This means that the current in the two resistors is the same.

3. The voltage difference across resistor A plus the voltage difference across resistor B adds up to the 10 volts across the pair. Very obvious.

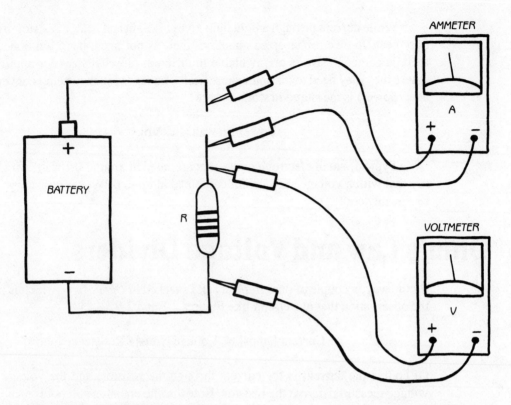

Figure 2-8   Pictorial diagram of battery-resistor circuit, showing ammeter and voltmeter in position for measurements.

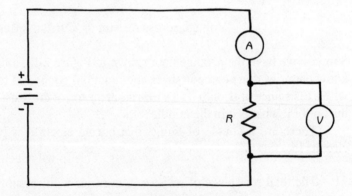

Figure 2-9   Schematic diagram of circuit shown in Figure 2-8.

Back to our determination of the middle voltage. Now we could grind through Ohm's Law, find the current passing through the circuit, then use the current to figure out what the voltage is across one of the resistors, which will tell us what the voltage is in the middle.

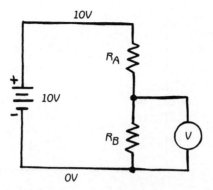

Figure 2-10   Diagram shows a "voltage divider" circuit.

However, there's no need to do that. Since the current through the two resistors is the same, and since the resistors have the same resistance, the voltage across each of the two resistors must also be the same. The total voltage is 10 volts, so each resistor must have 5 volts across it! The voltage in the middle must be 5 volts.

We can make this observation more general for cases where the resistances are not equal. Suppose the bottom resistor was 1 kilohm, and the top resistor was 9 kilohms, as shown in Figure 2-11. The current is the same in both resistors, so the voltage across the 9-kilohm resistor must be 9 times that across the 1-kilohm resistor. If you didn't guess the answer already:

Voltage across 9k ohms + voltage across 1k ohms = 10 volts
$9 \times$ "X" $+ 1 \times$ "X" = 10 volts
$(9+1) \times$ "X" = 10, obviously "X" = 1 here

So the voltage across the lower resistor is 1 volt, and across the upper it's 9 volts.

The generalization is that in a pair of resistors connected as shown in Figure 2-11, the voltage across the two resistors is divided between the two resistors according to the ratio of the two resistors. This is why such an arrangement is called a *voltage divider*.

Let us anticipate what is to come later by supposing that this voltage at the junction of the two resistors is of particular interest. For this type of situation, you should start to think of the resistor which is connected to the "high" voltage (10V in this case) as a *pull-up* resistor, because it pulls the voltage up. Similarly, the resistor connected to the "low" voltage is the *pull-down* resistor, pulling the voltage down. In the 9k-1k example, the pull-down was stronger than the pull-up, so the voltage at the junction ended up closer to the "low" voltage.

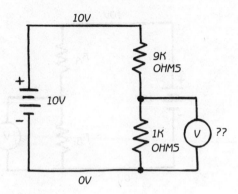

Figure 2-11   Same voltage divider arrangement, but this time with unequal resistors.

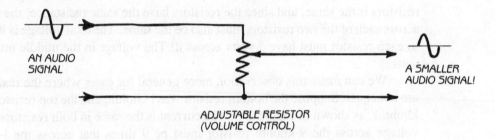

Figure 2-12   A variable voltage divider, which is a simple potentiometer (pot), is what controls the volume in your stereo.

What Use Is a Voltage Divider?

With two resistors and a battery we can do such not-so-amazing things as dividing the battery voltage to make new voltages. Far more usefully, what if, instead of a battery, we were feeding in a signal voltage?

Suppose, for example, that the incoming signal was the audio signal inside a stereo set. Using a voltage divider, we can reduce the size of the signal. In fact this is exactly how a volume control works, except that instead of two fixed resistors, the volume control is a single resistor with an adjustable midpoint (called a *potentiometer* or *pot*), providing a variable ratio by which to vary the volume (Figure 2-12).

We now have the capability to make signals of reduced sizes. But with our "high-low" digital signals surely this is something we do *not* want to do? This is exactly true, but we can use the voltage-divider concept to understand certain characteristics of the inputs and outputs we'll be encountering, which may cause our signals to become smaller undesirably.

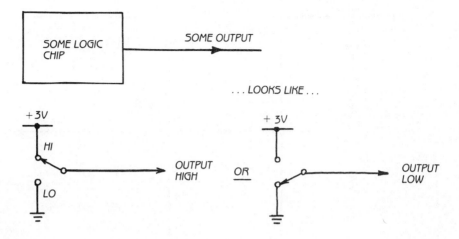

Figure 2-13a   Some output looks like. . .

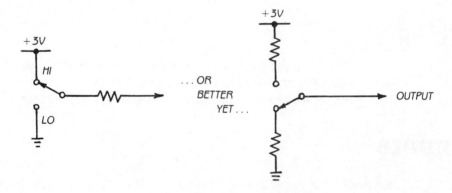

Figure 2-13b   . . .but actually more like this. . .   **Figure 2-13c**   . . .or better yet like this.

Outputs

So far as we have been concerned to this point, a digital output might look like a switch, switching between a "high" voltage, and a "low" voltage, Figure 2-13a. This sort of game where we say that so-and-so looks like a simple such-and-such is a favorite pastime of electronics engineers in their quest to make things simple enough to understand and work with. The simplified versions are often called *models*.

The truth of the matter is that real digital outputs are somewhat limited in the amount of current that they can supply to whatever might be hooked up. So to our simplified picture we add a resistor, as in Figure 2-13b. In fact, many digital outputs have *different* limitations in the "high" and "low" states, so Figure 2-13c is more applicable.

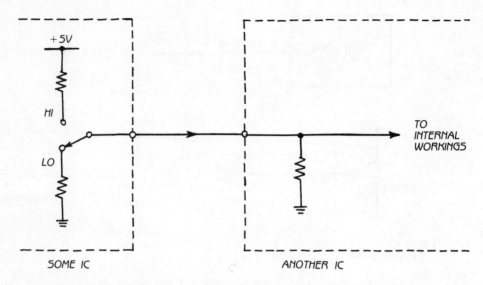

Figure 2-14 What if a resistor-to-ground was attached to a typical output?

These models point out that if for some reason a resistor is attached from the output to ground, as in Figure 2-14, then we essentially have a voltage-divider action going on which reduces the signal in a generally undesirable fashion.

Inputs

Ideally an input would permit no current to flow in or out of itself, so as not to disrupt the output to which it is connected. This input would merely "observe" the wire to which it was connected. As an example, oscilloscopes and digital volt-meters are built almost perfectly in this respect, so as not to disturb the circuitry they are observing.

Inputs, however, are not normally ideal, and generally have some sort of input current requirements, which can be represented with a resistor, as in Figure 2-15.

Outputs Connected to Inputs

In Figure 2-16, we see an example of an output connected to an input, with the output and input resistances shown. You can clearly see the voltage divider in play, working to reduce the magnitude of the signal available.

As a final step, I am going to show the actual output-input situations for several of the types of signals which are the subject of this book. I am *not* going to touch upon the actual meaning or activities of the particular signals, just how the electrical operation looks. Much more information is available about each in the individual chapters later on in the book.

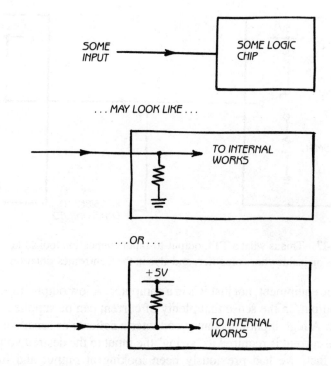

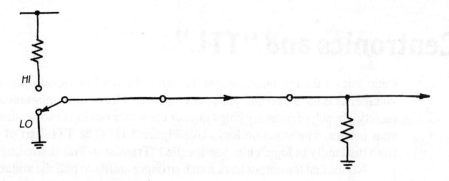

Figure 2-15   The input on a typical logic chip may not be ideal, that is, it may look like a resistor to ground, or to the power-supply.

Figure 2-16   Here is the combination of our output "model" connected to our input model.

Input and Output Impedances

As the preceding discussions have shown, the output "strength" and input "delicacy" are characteristics of great interest to designers, and to us if we are to perform some sophisticated troubleshooting. These two characteristics are often referred to as the output *impedance* and input *impedance*, and apply to all kinds of

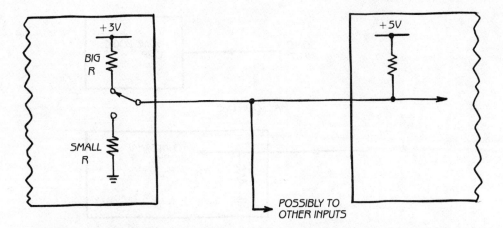

Figure 2-17   This is what a TTL output-to-input connection looks like. This is typical of what goes on inside your computer, and also in the Centronics situation.

electronic equipment, not just ICs in a computer. A low output impedance implies a strong output, in the sense that plenty of current can be supplied at the operating voltages. A high input impedance connotes a delicate or sensitive input, meaning that little current is required to "swing" the input to the desired voltage.

In fact, we had previously been looking at output and input resistance. Impedance is essentially just a more complicated specification of the characteristics of an output or input. For our purposes the simpler idea of resistance will suit quite adequately.

Centronics and "TTL"

Centronics links use more or less the same standard of signal outputs and input voltages as is used internally in your computer. Hence the communications link is merely a bunch of ordinary chips in your computer talking to some similar chips in your printer. The situation looks like Figure 2-17. (The TTL part of the name is from the family of logic chips used, called "Transistor-Transistor-Logic.")

Notice that the output has a much stronger ability to pull the voltage to the low state (lower resistance in the model) than to the high state. This is matched by a pull up resistor in the input connected to it. Notice also that if nothing is connected to such a TTL input, the built-in, pull-up resistor will pull up the input to a high state. This can be very significant when accidentally or deliberately leaving TTL inputs unconnected. (Occasionally such unconnected inputs will *not* "float" high, or may actually wander between high and low! Thus it is recommended to wire them either high or low.)

Although our TTL output is modeled with a switch and some resistors, in fact, the internal chip circuitry cannot stand certain mishaps, such as being shorted to +5 volts. Neither outputs nor inputs can stand being connected to any voltage

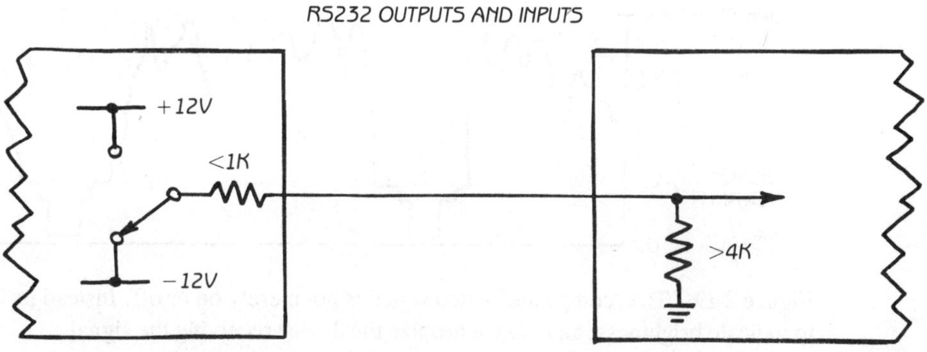

RS232 OUTPUTS AND INPUTS

Figure 2-18   RS-232 output and input models.

much outside the range 0 to 5 volts, which is why they are harmed by accidental connection to RS-232 outputs. If an input or output is damaged, there is no choice but to replace the defective chip.

One last interesting fact: if two TTL outputs accidentally become shorted together, then if one is trying to pull high and the other to pull low, the pull low will win because of the better pull-down ability. This sometimes makes for interesting symptoms.

A summary and comparison of the characteristics of various families of logic follows later.

RS-232 Serial

The outputs and inputs which make up a typical RS-232 arrangement look like Figure 2-18. Notice that the high and low voltages which are output are +12 volts and −12 volts respectively (approximately). By comparison, a real RS-232 input interprets anything above 3 volts as a "high", and anything below −3 volts as a "low."

Most RS-232 inputs are pulled toward ground (zero volts), which has no legitimate meaning, and results in an unpredictable interpretation of that input when it is left unconnected. To avoid this problem, for input wires which may not always be connected, manufacturers sometimes include an extra pull-up resistor to pull the input to the high state (which happens to be the state necessary to keep things running smoothly).

Video

Some video lines are simply TTL-like, as already described in the "Centronics" section. However other video signals look like Figure 2-19. In this figure, the output is not represented by a switch, because this type of video signal is "continu-

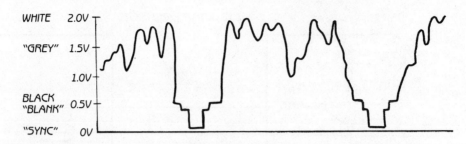

Figure 2-19   The "composite" video signal is not merely on or off. Instead its level varies to indicate brightness, and to synchronize the device receiving the signal.

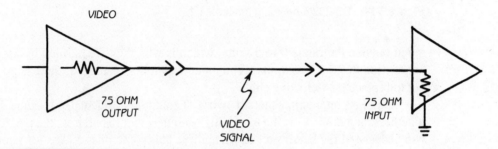

Figure 2-20   A simple model for video, showing an amplifier with 75-ohm output resistor, and a receiver with 75-ohm input.

ous." That is to say, the signal is not just high or low, but information is conveyed by intermediate levels also, like the brightness of a particular location on the screen.

Because of this, the output is shown (Figure 2-20) as a general amplifier symbol (the triangle), followed by a resistor, again to indicate how strongly or weakly the actual output wire is "pulled around."

Beyond this, the subject of video signals is somewhat involved, so it is left for its own section.

Various Logic Configurations and Families

As alluded to previously, TTL is not the only logic family in the world. It will be useful to compare notes on the characteristics of each for some of the later topics in the book. Of particular importance are understanding what sort of signals are to be expected in each case, (so we can set up test gadgets) and which families can talk to which others if need be. We may also want to feed in or get out signals for our own custom applications, as in Chapter 21.

If you are so inclined, you may wish to obtain some other books on logic, including manufacturer's data books. Also, there are a number of electronics and computer magazines with ideas on projects which can be built using these inexpensive and interesting devices. Some more comments on obtaining components and information is given in Chapter 21, Custom Connections.

Specifications: For each family, we will be interested in the characteristics of the input and output. For the input, we will be interested in the ranges of voltage which will be accepted as a "high" and a "low". In addition, we will want to know how much current the input will require in each of these states.

For the output, we will want to know what voltage it will put out for highs and lows, and how much current in each case. Here is a list of the characteristics with an explanation of their use:

Input High Voltage Range: Minimum voltage accepted as a logic high.

Input High Current: Maximum current into the input needed for a high.

Input Low Voltage Range: Maximum voltage accepted as a logic low.

Input Low Current: Maximum current out of input for low.

Output High Voltage: Minimum voltage which will be output as a high.

Output High Current: Minimum current ability (out) available when high.

Output Low Voltage: Maximum voltage which will be output as low.

Output Low Current: Minimum current ability (in) available when low.

Note that the currents listed above are simply another way of looking at the resistors in the models. For example, the Input Low Current refers to the current which must be drawn from the input in order to pull down against the influence of a built-in, pull-up resistor. Also, current into an IC pin will be called negative, and out from will be called positive.

In general usage, a designer rarely refers to these figures. Instead, he or she merely remembers how many inputs can be driven from one output of the same family, and this number is referred to as the *fan out*. This is fine so long as one family is not communicating with another dissimilar family. In that case calculations must be performed.

Also, in a real circuit with an output connected to multiple inputs, the actual voltages will vary depending upon how loaded the output is because of the effort of driving all of the inputs. The specs tell us how far we can go in asking a particular output to perform.

Here are several of the logic families:

Standard TTL

Power Supply Voltage: 5 volts ± 5%

	Input	Output	Units
High Voltage:	2.0	2.4	volts
High Current:	− 40	+ 800	μA (microamps)
Low Voltage:	0.8	0.4	volts
Low Current:	+ 1.6	− 16	mA (milliamps)

Fan Out: 10 TTL

TTL is the founding family of modern logic chips. TTL itself is rarely used in small computers any more because of its relatively high power consumption. However, the extensive group of functions for which TTL chips were made, and the particular pin connections used, have been followed for newer families. TTL chips have part numbers beginning with "74," such as 7400 and 74273.

LSTTL: Low Power Schottky TTL

Power Supply Voltage: 5 volts ± 5%

	Input	Output	Units
High Voltage:	2.0	2.4	volts
High Current:	− 20	+ 400	μA (microamps)
Low Voltage:	0.8	0.4	volts
Low Current:	+ 0.36	− 8.0	mA (milliamps)

Fan Out: 20 LSTTL

This is by far the most widely used logic family in small computers. It is faster than TTL, yet uses less power. Notice how the input and output voltage levels are essentially the same as for TTL, but output and input currents are less.

CMOS: (Complementary Metal Oxide Semiconductor, For What It's Worth)

Power Supply Voltage: 3 volts to 15 volts. The following are specs for 5 volt supply:

	Input	Output	Units
High Voltage:	3.3	5	volts
High Current:	0	+1	mA (milliamps)
Low Voltage:	1.7	0	volts
Low Current:	0	-1	mA (milliamps)

Fan Out: A large number of CMOS

The CMOS logic family has been quietly sitting around for many years now. It has some wonderful characteristics: extremely low power and operation from a wide range of supply voltages (ideal for battery power), outputs which swing from one supply voltage to ground, and inputs that draw almost no current. And to add to these virtues, the CMOS families have a variety of more sophisticated functions than the TTL families.

Unfortunately, CMOS is not very speedy, especially when run on only 5 volts. At 5 volts, some chips poop out at around 5 million transitions a second, which is not fast enough for operation directly with microprocessors.

There are a couple of venerable CMOS families, including one line whose numbers run in the 4000s, another family in the 4500s (these two sometimes appear as 14000s and 14500s). There is also a not-too-popular line of CMOS chips which provide the functions and pin connections of TTL parts, numbered 74C, like 74C00.

Note that although the available output current appears small, one has to examine to what output voltage these current specs apply. In fact, the currents given above apply to ouput voltages of 0.4 volt low, and 4.6 volts high. If it is permissible to have lower highs or higher lows, then more current capability is available. It is possible to get out 10 mA for an LED for example, if the series resistor is chosen appropriately.

HC and HCT: CMOS in TTL Clothing

Power Supply Voltage: 2 volts to 6 volts. Specs for 5 volt supply:

	HCT Input	HC Input	Output	Units
High Voltage:	2.0	3.5	5	volts
High Current:	0	0	+4	mA (milliamps)
Low Voltage:	0.8	1.0	0	volts
Low Current:	0	0	−4	mA (milliamps)

Fan Out: A large number of like parts.

As of this writing, these two High speed CMOS (HC) families have recently been introduced, but appear destined to become the dominant family. They are made using CMOS techniques, yet require a stricter power supply voltage. They require very little power, and almost no input current, yet run at speeds equivalent to LSTTL. A full line of functions is appearing, with numbers borrowed from both the TTL line (eg: 74HC645) and the CMOS line (74HCT4017).

The HC family provides inputs after the fashion of traditional CMOS, which is to say "high" and "low" are more or less above and below the 2/3 and 1/3 supply voltage points, respectively. The HCT family is similar in most respects, but the input voltages follow the TTL conventions, although the currents required are virtually nonexistent.

As with the older CMOS families, it is possible to obtain much greater output current if it is permissible to have worse high and low output voltages. 25 mA or more can be obtained within the range of allowable low or high voltages (as seen by an input).

Special Output Cases: Three-State and Open-Collector Output

There are a couple of special cases which are worth mentioning. Both are means by which multiple outputs can send signals on the same wires, although only one at a time.

The first method is used very widely inside the computer for communications on the data bus between the microprocessor and memory and the various support chips. In this case, the communication might be from micro to memory one microsecond, and from memory to micro the next. In order to achieve this with only one set of wires, the devices at each end must be able to perform as both inputs and outputs. These are referred to as *bidirectional I/O lines*. Other devices may never input from the bus, but nonetheless have output capability.

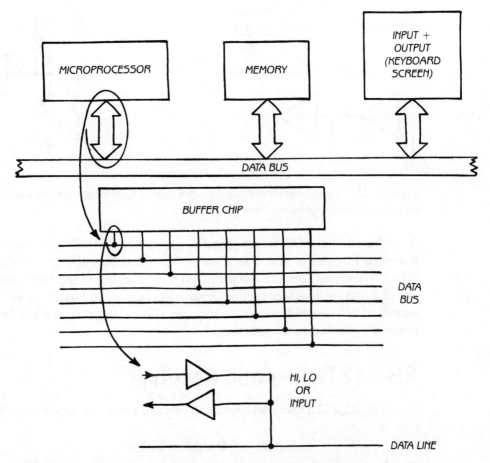

Figure 2-21 Simplified drawing of a computer showing the data bus plus each chip with its three-state, I/O lines.

The outputs of such chips are referred to as *three-state*, because they can pull high, pull low, or simply "do nothing," effectively disconnecting themselves from the bus (Figure 2-21). There are members of all logic families which have three-state ability. When designing a computer, it is a matter of great concern to ensure that each chip, which is physically connected to the data bus is properly controlled so that it outputs only in its turn.

An older, but still useful, convention is sometimes used where multiple devices must all output on the same wire. This convention is referred to as *open collector* (OC). In this convention, each output only has the abilities to pull down, or do nothing. In this case, whatever information is to be communicated is best signalled by a low signal. An example of OC is illustrated in Figure 2-22.

This OC convention might be used in a situation where any of the attached outputs is allowed to signal at any time. This scheme is typically used in multiboard systems (although not the IBM-PC) where any one board might wish to signal an interrupt to the main processor.

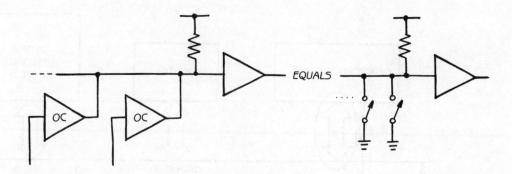

Figure 2-22   Open collector outputs are often used in simple applications where multiple outputs must communicate with one input.

Contrastingly, OC outputs might be used in a system where only one output is permitted to signal at any time. This is the case in the cabling of multiple disk drives. There, only one drive is permitted to send signals to the main controller at any time, but the lines used for this signalling are shared among all drives. Thus the outputs of the selected drive are the only ones allowed to pull low, while the outputs of the other drives are doing nothing.

RS-232 Driver and Receiver

The RS-232 Driver and Receiver specifications are listed here for comparison.

	Input	Output	Units
High Voltage:	3	12	volts
High Current:	−3	+12	mA (milliamps)
Low Voltage:	−3	−12	volts
Low Current:	+3	−12	mA (milliamps)

Fan Out: Not generally of concern.

Hooking a Switch to a Logic Input

The models I have presented often show a logic output as though it was a switch. On some occasions, it is actually desired to connect a switch to a logic input and, from the models and the information on the various logic families, it can be seen that this is a straightforward job. Although this will be described in more detail in Chapters 20 and 21, Figure 2-23 gives some examples.

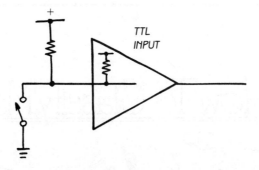

Figure 2-23a   When hooking a switch to a TTL input, it is most natural to use a pull-up resistor and have the switch pull this to ground when closed.

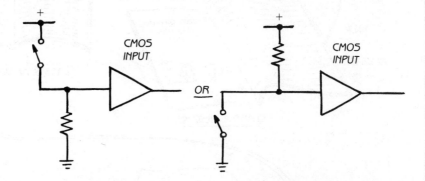

Figure 2-23b   With CMOS, the input is not predisposed to pull high or low, so a switch can be wired either way.

How To Classify Manuals.

CLASS A: MISTAKE.

CLASS B: AMBIGUITY

CLASS C: OMISSION

CLASS D: THE PROJECT COMPLETED.
(TOO FEW KNOWN EXAMPLES TO BE
ABLE TO DEPICT ANYTHING.)

3

Cautions About Equipment Documentation

If you are going to use technical manuals, you should know how and why they are so poor. You can then anticipate the sort of errors you might encounter and take steps to correct them. I explain here why the manuals are wrong in the hope that you will be convinced not to take them at face value.

Here, then, is a description of how manuals get to be wrong.

To begin, imagine how the manual got produced. First of all, the piece of equipment (computer, printer, etc.) was designed and built. Then somebody had to produce a manual. The manual is often the last annoying thing to be done before the product can be shipped out and sold, so it is produced in a hurry.

Who writes the manual? Here we have a selection of possibilities. It could have been written by some new engineer who isn't allowed to do any real design work as yet. Or, if the company is larger, it might have been cranked out by the "documentation department." Another possibility is that it was created by some outside, commercial art outfit. In all of these cases, the manual was created by people neither intimately involved with the product, nor responsible for making the product work. They are also probably not familiar with RS-232, Centronics, video or any of the other interfaces as they really exist.

You should also understand how proofreading works. Once a manual has been typed or typeset, it is necessary for someone to read over the work to see if it is correct. However, this often is *not* a process of checking against the original manuscript, since that is extremely time consuming and a headache. Proofreading sometimes amounts to just reading over the text for obvious typographical and spelling errors which the proofreader happens to recognize. As a consequence, you might see "modem" turned into "modern" and "baud" turned into "band" as the proofreader misses the typist's mistakes, or intentionally "corrects" these unfamiliar, technical words. Who knows what can happen to minute details, like the distinction between DCE and DTE and mentions of specific pin numbers.

From these general principles, we can see several specific types of problems. If you are aware of these problems, then, hopefully, you will be able to spot areas where you should not be too confident in the technical manuals you encounter.

Gallery of Technical Mangles

The following are just some of the many possible manual mangles:

1. The writer may have been good at describing how to unpack the printer, but didn't understand the first thing about computers or interfaces, especially RS-232. This usually leads to a literal transcription of someone elses' scribbled notes, a transcription from a dictation machine, or completely skirting the issue. My favorite dictation mistake appeared in an article about a computerized analysis, reported to be a "four-year analysis". It was nothing so lengthy, just a "Fourier analysis" with a very American accent.

2. The writer knew about the Official Standard, (like RS-232C) and proceeded to tell about it, so convinced of his knowledge of the standard that he overlooked the fact that, on his company's equipment, it was implemented differently.

3. The design of the machine was changed in production, but the manual was not.

4. The technical manual was good, but didn't come with the unit.

5. The manual was very comprehensive, but so disorganized that you have to make separate notes as you read the hundreds of pages involved in order to collect the necessary, small group of information needed for your application.

6. The manual looks very pretty. Unfortunately, the technical details were also typeset for appearance, and now you can't tell the ones and zeroes from "elles" and "ohs." Nor can you see where the spaces are located in the example programs.

7. The manual was translated from Japanese (or another language), and lost something in the translation. In a recent episode, we received a Japanese printer largely labelled "SERIAL." Unfortunately, this was actually a printer with a *parallel* interface. The SERIAL on the box came from the fact that it prints dots "serially" across the paper (the way all dot-matrix printers do!).

8. The manual tells you everything, except for one minor (but operation-blocking) detail. This frequently happens. Perhaps after you hook up the printer, you have to type some "secret" code, like CTRL-I 7 P CTRL-I 1 D or some such.

9. In the typing or typesetting process, certain symbols were left out to be placed in the text later, but never got put in. These include the "bars" which are sometimes placed over signals to indicate inversion, Greek symbols, and others.

The point to all this is: *Be prepared to disbelieve the manual.* Don't drop your guard just because the manual looks expensive, or because the computer was mass-produced. Always try to check what the manual says against something else. If you can read a schematic diagram, check what the text says about the connector against the schematic. If two descriptions of the connector are given (such as a connector picture and a pin-versus-signal table), then check one against the other. Check what the manual says against what you would expect. And finally, when you come to hooking things up the way the manual suggests and it doesn't work, test the signals to see if the manual is in error.

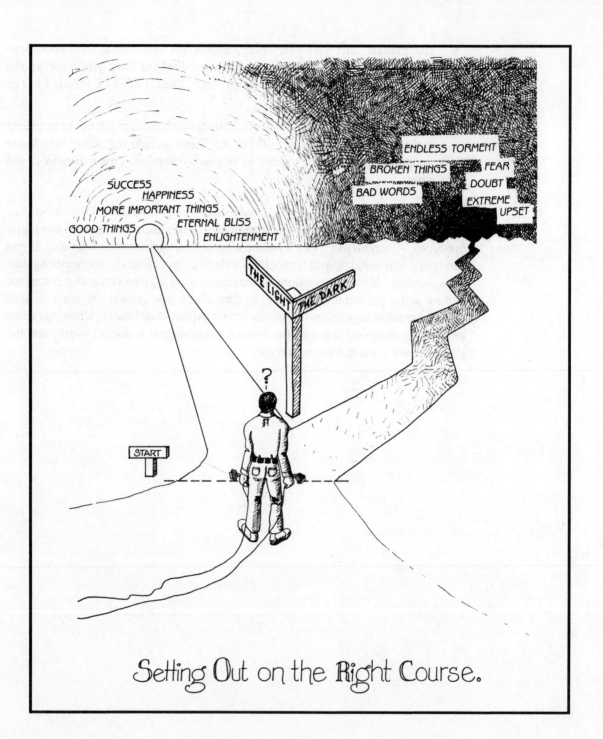

Setting Out on the Right Course.

4

Attacking RS-232: Setting Out on the Right Course

Throughout this chapter, we will assume that the task at hand is to get two pieces of equipment connected together and talking satisfactorily. These might be computer-to-printer, terminal-to-modem, graphics tablet-to-computer, or whatever. All of these situations are amenable to the same basic strategy.

Some Vocabulary

RS-232C: The latest version of the real RS-232 standard is called RS-232C. Since this book is about the hacked-over versions of RS-232 usually encountered in the popular computer-system arena, I will refer to the interface as RS-232X — "X" for unknown. Note that this is just my own terminology.

Machine: Because there is no single word meaning "piece of electronic or computer equipment," the word "machine" has been stolen. Don't picture that a machine has to have motors and gears. I also use the word "equipment" as a singular noun: "he connected equipment A to equipment B."

Interface: This is a very overworked word. The reader should understand with a certain degree of sympathy that the computer "explosion" has led to a word shortage. Things have appeared which needed names faster than good names could be thought up. So, you will find some things called by new, silly names, and other names which are used for several different purposes.

"Interface" has a number of different meanings. In general, they are all tied to the theme that information is being converted from one form to another, or transported from one machine to another. Thus, RS-232, in general, might be described as an "interface scheme"; it provides an "interface" between two machines. On the other hand, if a certain printer needs a special circuit-board installed to make it talk RS-232X, then that board might be referred to as an "interface card," or simply as an "RS-232 interface." In the first case, RS-232 provides the interface between the two machines; in the second case, the board provides the interface between the printer's internal intelligence and the RS-232 connector. Finally, some people sloppily refer to the RS-232 connector on the back panel as "the RS-232 interface."

Serial: RS-232 is what is known as a "serial" interface. Don't worry if that doesn't mean anything to you yet, I'll explain it later. By contrast, the Centronics-type interface, sometimes used for printers, belongs to a different group known as "parallel" interfaces. Often, when referring to printers which may be purchased with either an RS-232 interface or a Centronics interface, sales literature may refer to the two simply as "serial" or "parallel." Technically this is ambiguous, since there are other forms of serial interface and other forms of parallel interface, however, the literature-reader is supposed to understand what is meant from the context.

DB25:   This is the style of connector generally used with RS-232X. It is D-shaped (use your imagination liberally), and it has 25 pins in two rows. The connector comes in male and female (the one with pins sticking out is the male). The female connector's contacts, despite the fact that they are actually pin-receptacles, are often referred to as "pins."

The Three RS-232 Jobs

You must turn your attention to three basic areas to successfully solve an RS-232X interface problem. The specifics of these areas may not be fully apparent to you at the moment, but I will endeavor to explain them in later chapters. The point here is to provide a comprehensive framework upon which you can hang all the little details. Here are the three areas to which I refer:

1. **Cabling:** Get the appropriate connector pins at one end connected to the appropriate pins at the other end. This job is the most obvious task associated with RS-232X, but is only one third of the journey.

2. **Options:** There are several characteristics of the communications process which may be varied. The two pieces of equipment must be set up so that they both agree on these matters. Here is a list of some of these options, which you may recognize:

   Number of bits

   Baud rate

Parity

Handshaking

X-ON X-OFF

ETX-ACK

and others. These options may be set by flipping switches or sometimes by running a configuring program.

3. **Software:** If one of the pieces of equipment is a computer, you will need to have available appropriate software to send something out of the RS-232X connector or to receive something into it. This might be as simple as knowing how to activate the printer using the BASIC programming language or from your word-processor program, or it might be as complicated as writing an assembly-language routine to handle serial character input/output for the operating system.

It is unlikely that such an assembly-language programming task would be necessary on the newer, more integrated computer systems (IBM-PC and Kaypro being examples). You are more likely to be faced with the task on S-100 systems, where the serial RS-232 interfaces are added to the system on a separate board, or where you are trying to do something unusual.

Check Your Tools

The following is a list of all the tools at your disposal in the attack on an RS-232X hook-up job:

Technical Manuals: Manuals on the particular machines involved should, in theory, provide all the info you need, and should make this book unnecessary. Unfortunately, the documentation for RS-232X is exceedingly poor. It is either missing, incomplete, ambiguous or wrong. The occasions when the documentation is completely correct are so exceptional as to be only a marginal help, since you don't know when it *is* correct!

General RS-232X Knowledge: This can be gained from this book. This allows you to challenge the machines' documentation intelligently. It also forms the basis for the strategies below.

RS-232X Strategies: Armed with a repertoire of strategies, such as those contained in this book, there is almost no RS-232X interface which you cannot make work if the capability exists in the two machines.

Trial Cable Kit: If you are making only one cable, you won't absolutely need this item. The trial cable is simply a cable which is specially set up to allow you to try different cross-connections quickly and easily. Commercial models are also referred to as *breakout-boxes*, and can cost up to $150. I'll show you a very quick way to put together your own trial cable which can be made cheaply, and should work better.

Observation Gadgets: Many of the strategies require the use of some sort of RS-232X observation gadget. These can be extremely simple, yet they serve the important function of being your eyes into RS-232X (you wouldn't fix your car with your eyes closed would you?). If you are the kind of person interested in making up your own cable, you won't mind a trip over to the local electronics emporium, nor the assembly of a simple gadget.

Cabling Bits and Pieces: You will need to obtain the connector parts for your cable. Several varieties are available. We will look at both the good stuff and the bad stuff.

HISTORY AS IT MIGHT HAVE BEEN

ELECTRONICS
INDUSTRY
ASSOCIATION

.... AND AFTER THE COMMITTEE HAD DECIDED UPON THE
SHAPE OF THE TABLE, 13 MEN SAT DOWN ON ONE SIDE,
AND 12 ON THE OTHER. ....

5

Obligatory Chapter on the "Official" RS-232 Standard

This chapter is very boring, and may be read in case of insomnia. It concerns the actual definition of RS-232 written by a committee of the Electronic Industries Association. This information is included because it covers the jargon names for the various wires used in RS-232, and misleadingly in the RS-232X. There is also a small amount of historical perspective to be gained.

The latest version of RS-232, called RS-232C, was arrived at in 1969 (for what that's worth). To add to the confusion, the International Telegraph and Telephone Consultative Committee (CCITT) have a standard called *V.24*, the results of an international effort. V.24 is essentially the same as RS-232, except, of course, that the signal names are different. It is unfortunate that the names are not in a foreign language, because if they were, they might cause us less problems.

To clarify the effect of this upon consumers, I propose that we rename the standard "RH-232" — "RH" for Red Herring.

What the Standards Say

First, equipment is referred to as being one of two sexes. These are known as *Data Terminal Equipment* and *Data Communications Equipment*. These are almost invariably called just *DTE* and *DCE*. Now, would you trust a committee who came up with two names which sound so much alike?

A terminal is a DTE, and a modem is a DCE. Note that the sex of the equipment does not imply that one is superior, or works differently from the other. It merely refers to the way the connector is wired. Indeed, two *computers* may talk to each other—as long as we get the cable right. Yet either one might have been manufactured as a DTE or DCE.

The whole idea of having two different sexes of connector was devised so that, in common situations, a "straight-through" cable can be used; that is, each pin on one end is wired to the like-numbered pin on the other end. This requires that outputs on one end match up to inputs on the other end. This is the way that terminals and modems are built and used.

The problems began when other pieces of equipment appeared with what were supposed to be RS-232 connectors. You used to be sure that a modem would connect to a DTE with a straight-through cable. Printers, plotters, digitizer pads, mice and other equipment, however, are not obviously DTEs or DCEs, so manufacturers have assigned genders to such equipment in an arbitrary fashion.

The Chart

The complete list of signals (Table 5-1) may seem baffling and complicated. However, only in relatively rare situations are all, or even most, of these signals present. That situation occurs only when a sophisticated modem is connected to a main-frame, time-share type of computer system. In such a system, the modems are complicated because they have to answer the phone line automatically, and perhaps tell the computer about signal quality, and so on.

For most equipment that you will encounter in the personal-computer market, only a small number of these signals are used, but they are implemented *very* inconsistently.

Warning Number 1: Signal names are not necessarily with respect to the piece of equipment you are looking at. For example, the wire carrying data from the terminal to the modem (Wire 2) is called "Transmitted Data." This seems appropriate when you encounter it in the terminal's manual because Pin 2 on the terminal is an output. If you come across it in the modem's manual, however, this may be confusing because the modem's Pin 2 will still be called "Transmitted Data," yet it is an *input* to the modem. This problem is accentuated when the manual does not use the exact name, but perhaps uses "Transmit Data," or "Data Out."

This confusion is multiplied in a situation where the equipment is not terminal and modem, but two small computers. Even if the manuals tell you that Computer A "emulates a DCE" and Computer B "emulates a DTE," it's very hard to sort out which are inputs and which are outputs based only on those morsels of information.

> **Warning Number 2:** In many cases, when a manual refers to a signal name (such as "SRTS") the manual quite often does not mean that particular function (Secondary Request To Send), but is using that name merely to refer to that particular connector pin (Pin 19 in this case). The pin might actually be used for a completely different purpose!

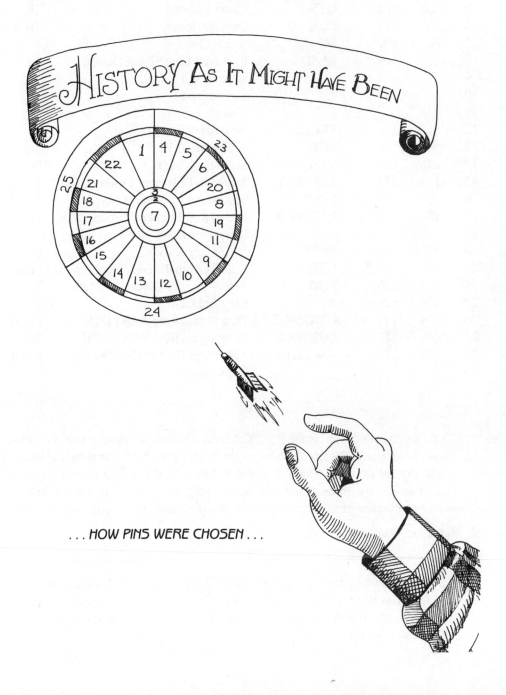

. . . HOW PINS WERE CHOSEN . . .

Table 5-1 Official RS-232/CCITT Nomenclature Table

Pin	Cct	CCITT	Abbrev	"Real" Name	To/From DTE
1	AA	101	PG	Protective Chassis Ground	---
2	BA	103	TxD	Transmitted Data	From
3	BB	104	RxD	Received Data	To
4	CA	105	RTS	Request To Send	From
5	CB	106	CTS	Clear To Send	To
6	CC	107	DSR	Data Set Ready	To
7	AB	102	SG	Signal Ground	---
8	CF	109	RLSD	Received Line Signal Detector	To
9				Unassigned	
10				Unassigned	
11				Unassigned	
12	SCF	122	SRLSD	Secondary RLSD	To
13	SCB	121	SCTS	Secondary CTS	To
14	SBA	118	STxD	Secondary TxD	From
15	DB	114	TSETDCE	Trans Sigl Element Timing DCE	To
16	SBB	119	SRxD	Secondary Received Data	To
17	DD	115	RSETDCE	Recvd Sigl Element Timing DCE	To
18				Unassigned	
19	SCA	120	SRTS	Secondary RTS	From
20	CD	108.2	DTR	Data Terminal Ready	From
21	CG	110	SQD	Signal Quality Detect	To
22	CE	125	RI	Ring Indicator	To
23	CH	111	DSRSDTE	Data Signal Rate Select DTE	From
23	CI	112	DSRSDCE	Data Signal Rate Select DCE	To
24	DA	113	TSETDTE	Trans Sigl Element Timing DTE	From
25				Unassigned	

Notes

1. The column called "Cct" is the RS-232 "circuit" name, as opposed to pin number or signal name. Essentially, the circuit name might be thought of as a name for the wire, so that we might say for example "Pin 4 is connected to wire CA which carries signal RTS." The circuit names are encountered relatively rarely, and even then are usually used only to refer to particular pins, as synonyms for the pin numbers or signal names.

2. Pin 23 has two official uses.

A common saying summarizing just about the only reliable piece of information from this table is "Two-terminal transmit." (Three other things fall into place: 3 on the terminal is receive, which makes 2 on the modem an input, and 3 on the modem an output.)

6

RS-232X Basic Strategy Step One: Selecting Options

In order to expand on the strategies you can use to get your interface job figured out, I have devised a two-level approach. The first level provides a simple understanding of how RS-232X works; the second level takes a more technical approach, and is covered in a later chapter.

Dealing with the Options

You may have to set certain options before your two devices will talk to each other. I am not going to describe what these options actually do at this stage (since that won't help you make a better decision); I'll just tell you the option names, comment on what choices you should expect and explain how to get an agreement. Note that these options are usually set by flipping little switches (often called *DIP* switches), or by moving tiny jumper connectors.

With personal computers, you are often provided with the manufacturer's software for setting up many options including the configuration of the serial ports: CP/M systems use STAT and perhaps another configuration-setting program like CONFIG or BAUD, and MSDOS/PCDOS systems use programs like CONFIGUR and MODE. Apple II Plus/e/c systems do strange things, depending upon the serial card you use. The popular Super Serial card may be set using switches or special command strings. Apple Macintosh applications generally have a window for setting serial-port parameters, while DECmates have a parameter-setting menu associated with their communications option. Many computers permit you to set up the serial port automatically each time you boot up.

The configuration might also be changed by different applications packages. For example, a "terminal" package might set up the serial port one way, while a word processor might set it up another way. Also, each package may not set it back the way it was before! These are all fun things to watch for.

Also note that, in the case of option switches and jumpers, you usually have to turn the equipment power off, then back on, before the new settings will take effect. This is because, inside most equipment, there is actually a microprocessor dedicated to the task of controlling that equipment. The switches do not control the indicated function directly; instead, they are merely inputs to the microprocessor. The micro looks at the switches when power first comes on, and uses that information to adjust its behavior accordingly. Thereafter, the switches are ignored.

Data Rate or Baud Rate: *Baud* is the unit name for measuring speed of communication in bits per second. Your choices are generally as follows: 110 baud, 150, 300, 600, 1200, 1800, 2400, 4800, 9600, and 19200 baud. The two communicating devices must agree on this. In general, you should use the highest number which both machines have available. Some equipment only works at one rate. Ordinary modems, for example, work at 300 baud. Other factors influence choice of rate, so if operation is unsatisfactory further thought will be necessary.

Number of Bits or Data Length: Your choice of *data bits* will be from 5 to 8, with 8 or 7 most common for newer equipment (5 or 6 bits were used with ancient teletypes). Both machines should agree, but may work (at least erratically) even without agreement. Other technical considerations will influence a preference between 7 or 8.

Number of Stop Bits: You will usually have a choice between 1, 1.5 or 2. Make the two devices agree, and choose one stop bit, if possible (1.5 is usually only used with 5-bit character length).

Parity: Your choices will be either Ignore (same as None), Even, Odd, Mark or Space. Choose Ignore on both machines if possible, otherwise select an agreeing choice. (Parity is an error-checking scheme, so it is most useful where the communications path is of dubious quality. Thus parity is sometimes used with modem-and-telephone communication. However, even with telephone communications, other more sophisticated error-checking schemes are often used, once again making parity unnecessary. The use of parity or some other error-checking scheme is generally made known to you when you log on to such a remote system.)

Mode (Full- or Half-Duplex):   This option is usually only encountered on terminals, or computers pretending to be terminals and on the modems to which they are attached. In *Full Duplex*, what you type on the keyboard is sent to the remote system, which immediately "echoes" back to your terminal what it received. It is this echo that appears on the screen, *not* what you typed directly. This method is used so you have an immediate visual verification that the remote system is awake, and that the communications are working. (For those of you who use time-share systems with passwords: it is the temporary cancellation of the echo which allows your entry of a password to be "invisible" on your screen.)

In *Half-Duplex*, what you type is placed on your screen by your own terminal, and it is expected that the remote system will *not* echo your characters. If it *does* echo them, you will see two characters on your screen for each one typed, and you will know to switch your terminal (or modem) to Full Duplex. Half Duplex is sometimes also called *Local Echo* (not to be confused with *Local Mode!*), while Full Duplex is sometimes called *Echoplex*.

Handshaking: (Hardware/XON-XOFF/ETX-ACK): This mouthful
is referred to as *handshaking* or, more appropriately, *flow control*. Flow control concerns methods by which one piece of equipment may control the flow of data coming to it from another piece of equipment, so as not to get overfilled.

If your setup needs flow control, you may have a choice of methods which could be employed. These are explained more fully in the next chapter on cabling. You sometimes get a choice as to which signals appear on which connector pins. You will have to decide this in conjunction with your cabling decisions. (In other words, more study is necessary for you on this subject.)

Occasionally you may be presented with a choice of *polarity* for DTR, CTS, DSR, or RTS; choose *Normal* (not inverted), or *positive*. (Even the meanings of Normal and Inverted are ambiguous in some manuals. Another comment on this in Chapter 7).

Carriage Return-Line Feed Options: While not strictly pertaining to
RS-232X, this matter is mentioned here because it is often chosen at option-selection time, using nearby switches or the same "configuration" software.

This option is generally encountered on terminals and printers. The basic choice is whether the end of a line of text will be signified by a Carriage Return character only (CR), or by the sequence Carriage Return-Line Feed (CR-LF). No harm will come if you make the wrong choice. You will merely end up with double-spaced text, or unspaced text writing over itself. You will know how to react by seeing the symptoms.

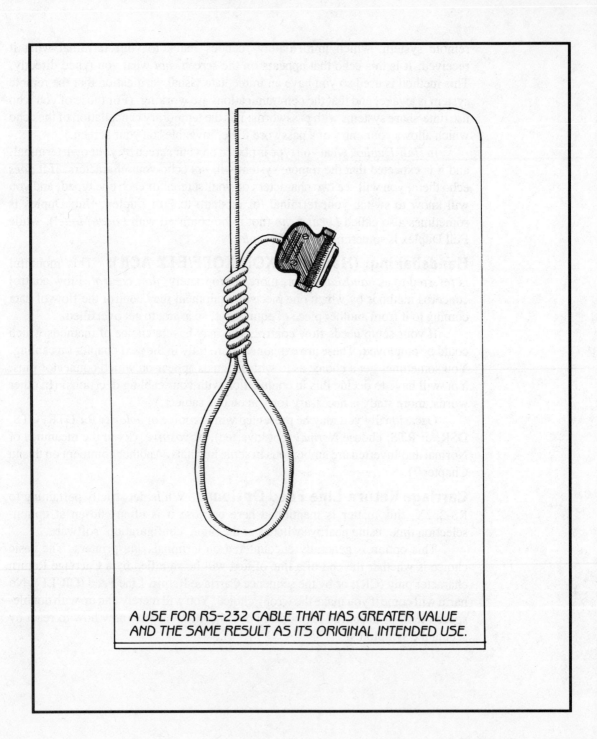

A USE FOR RS–232 CABLE THAT HAS GREATER VALUE
AND THE SAME RESULT AS ITS ORIGINAL INTENDED USE.

7

RS-232X Basic Strategy Step Two: Simple Cabling

Finally, we arrive at what many may consider to be the meat of the matter: the actual handling of cable and connectors. For purposes of speed, we can divide applications into two areas:

1. ordinary terminal to ordinary modem

2. everything else in the world

Ordinary Terminal to Ordinary Modem

This is, of course, the application for which RS-232 was actually conceived, and to which it usually applies fairly consistently. It even applies to hooking a modem to a computer, *provided* that the computer's modem connector is specified to be a DTE (terminal-like) connection. So, lucky you, very little more needs to be understood about the setup. You can build or obtain a *straight-through* cable and be pretty sure it will work. Such a cable has every pin connected to the like-numbered pin on the other end (Pin 1 to Pin 1, Pin 2 to Pin 2 and so on).

This straight-through cable can be made using ribbon cable and IDC connectors, or solder-type connectors (see Chapter 11 on RS-232 Cable and Connectors). If you make a straight-through cable using the solder-type connectors, you can save a lot of work by wiring only those pins that are used on both ends. In almost all cases, you will need only 1-1, 2-2, 3-3, 4-4, 5-5, 6-6, 7-7, 8-8, and 20-20, as shown in Figure 7-1.

Before assembling, be sure to check the sex of the connectors required. Terminals are supposed to be male (on the terminal) and modems are supposed to be female, but this is often not the case.

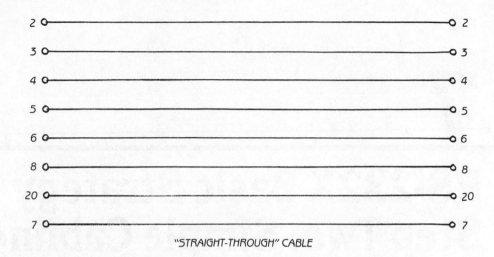

"STRAIGHT-THROUGH" CABLE

Figure 7-1 A straight-through cable. Usually, these are all the wires you need in such a cable.

Everything Else in the World

Now, we have to start using the old intellect. Other books and articles about RS-232 systems divide the various classes of equipment based upon the type of cable which will be suitable. In my view, this is rather pointless; most of the time, you won't know what class you are dealing with until you have gone through the exercise of determining what sort of cable is needed!

How Much Do You Know Already?

The remainder of this chapter describes the functions of the various wires involved in RS-232X. Methods will be presented for progressing toward a working cable, assuming you have *no* information about the connector arrangement of either piece of equipment. Of course, you usually have some information from the equipments' manuals, so you may not have to be so devious. The point is this: if you understand the signals involved, and the techniques which can be used to verify that they work as expected, then, it is less likely that you will be led astray by erroneous documentation.

One of the strategies available is to rig up a cable and try it out. This can be done by actually wiring a cable as you would a finished version; however, this is tedious to change. Many people make or buy a trial-cable kit which can be quickly configured without soldering. Such a cable is shown in Chapter 9 along with actual construction details.

> **A piece of friendly advice:** if working with electronics and the technical end of computers is new to you, please do *not* believe that, in this kind of work, you can simply follow cookbook directions and come up with a working solution. It is only remotely possible that the result will work immediately. The satisfying, efficient way to work is to proceed step-by-step, checking at each step of the way that what happens is what you thought would happen. This is very much like building furniture: when you're finishing the piece, you sand a bit, then you feel and look at the work to ensure that it is right. You alternate between sanding and inspecting until you are satisfied with the result.

This tells us that we must not simply know what we are *supposed* to do, but also how to *check each step*.

Write It Down!

As you proceed with these tests and trials, be sure to keep notes on what you discover about each pin at each end. A form for this purpose, which you may photocopy, is included in the appendix.

It is now time to examine the RS-232 signals, what they do, and how they should be connected. In other words, we will look at the cable-to-be wire- by-wire and pin-by-pin, until a complete specification is built for the cable.

Signal Ground (Pin 7)

There are two *ground* wires. One is called *Signal Ground*, and it is on Pin 7. It is essential to operation. It provides the "reference" upon which interpretation of the data-carrying and other signals is based.

Protective Ground (Pin 1)

The "other" ground is called *Protective Ground*, located on Pin 1. Inside each piece of equipment it is supposed to be connected to the "chassis" ground, which in turn should be internally connected to the third (long) prong on the power cord. You are supposed to wire it through in the cable for safety reasons; however, it doesn't have any bearing on the operation of the RS-232 signals. Many times it is not used, and sometimes it is just internally connected to Pin 7 anyway.

Is it safe to leave Pin 1 unconnected? If both pieces of equipment have three-wire power cords (plugged into proper three-hole wall sockets), then any protection afforded by the Pin 1 connection is redundant.

There are perhaps two types of situations where Pin 1 is useful. If by some chance, the chassis' of the two pieces of equipment, are *not* connected to the same ground, then a voltage may exist between the two equipments which might damage the circuitry connected to the signal lines. If one or both equipments are not grounded at all, then this Pin-1 wire will provide the connection to bring both equipments to the same voltage for operation which will not damage the components. This implies, however, that the non-grounded equipment is working improperly in the first place, and should be repaired anyway.

The second possible service of the Pin-1 wire is where you are using shielded cable, particularly in long runs through walls or ceilings. In that case, you can connect the shield to Pin 1 (note that Pin 7 should always be carried on a separate wire, **not** the shield). First, this allows the shield to keep electrical noise out of the signal wires properly. On the safety side, if a mishap should occur, and some high-voltage wire (perhaps 110 volts) were to slash into the cable, it would come in contact with the grounded shield, first. If you are lucky, this short-to-ground will blow a fuse somewhere before the high-voltage wire has a chance to contact the damageable signal wires.

You should know that these scenarios are optimistic. For the Pin-1 ground to give us protection, it must be capable of carrying a fair bit of current. An inspection of the size and gripping force of a single DB-25 connecting pin should convince you that this is hardly the case!

So, Pin 1 is rather an enigma. It certainly is useful for keeping out electrical noise in shielded cables, but for safety, its necessity is debatable. If you are worried, connect it through. However, it would seem more important to have three-wire line cords on the equipment, and to insure a safe path for the signal cable.

The Data Lines (Pins 2 and 3)

In RS-232X, only two wires are used to carry data, one for each direction. These will always be on Pin 2 or 3. In fact, for a simple one-way data path (computer to printer, for example) only one data line may be used, resulting in a cable having a total of just two wires, Data and Ground. Many other situations will require two-way communications, which means both Pins 2 and 3 are used. You will need to determine whether these will be connected in your cable as 2-2 and 3-3, or 2-3 and 3-2.

Digression on What To Do About Pin Choices

With the data lines, we have encountered the first set of signals where we have confusion. We don't immediately know whether Machine A's Pin 2 should go to Machine B's Pin 2 or Pin 3, and vice versa. Our goal is to hook A's output (whichever that is) to B's input, and B's output to A's input.

If you are lucky, you will have both manuals, and they will both tell you which of 2 and 3 is an input, and which is an output. You can proceed from there. Alternatively, it's possible that a manual will say something like "this machine emulates a DTE." You can then refer to Table 5-1 and note that Pin 2 is the data output. Often, however, the manual will say that Pin 2 is TxD, but if it doesn't tell whether this is a DTE or a DCE, you are none the wiser.

There will be further comments on trial cables, and what to do about these mystery choices.

Digression on Signal States

A word is in order regarding the "states" of the data signals. Although not explained here fully, exposure to the terminology may be helpful.

Here is where I hope that you understood at least some of what I covered in the "Philosophy of Electronics" in Chapter 2. Recall that data (characters) are stored in a computer's memory as a collection of ones and zeroes. It should be no big surprise, then, that data appears on an RS-232X data line as a series (hence, the name "serial") of zeroes and ones. Of course, those zeroes and ones are actually just two distinct states, which happen to be two distinct voltages.

The two distinct voltages are $+12$ volts and -12 volts, approximately. In RS-232 jargon, $+12$ volts is referred to as *space* and -12 volts is referred to as *mark*. On a data line, Space represents a zero, and Mark represents a one. When no data is flowing, a data line sits at Mark. (Note: because Mark and Space are difficult to remember, most of us refer to them as simply Low and High.)

	Voltage	RS-232 Name	Data meaning
Low	-12V	Mark	One
High	$+12$V	Space	Zero

This is, obviously, only a stop-gap explanation. A fuller story is given in Chapter 8.

The Flow-Control (Handshaking) Lines

What happens if your computer is sending text to a printer, and the printer can't print fast enough to keep up? Most printers have a built-in *memory buffer* which stores characters as they come in until they can be printed, but it's quite possible that your computer could fill up that buffer, and then what? This problem occurs in other devices as well.

The answer to this dilemma is called *handshaking*, or, more recently, and properly, *flow control*. Unfortunately, there are several ways to accomplish this function, which makes things confusing. The following examples discuss the problem using a computer and a printer, but the details are generally applicable to other sorts of equipment.

One way to handle flow control is to have a wire from the printer to the computer saying "Hey, stop the flow until I say go again." This is referred to as a *hardware handshake line* (to distinguish it from certain other flow-control schemes, which will be described later). Some systems may have provision for two levels of hardware flow control: one wire to indicate that the equipment (perhaps the printer) is switched off, and the other wire to indicate a temporary hold-up, such as buffer full.

There are two important conclusions to be noted here. First, when figuring out the cable, you may anticipate the possibility of one (occasionally two) line going *in* to a device which can prevent that device from sending data *out*. If these wires are not handled correctly, the unit will not send anything out! Secondly, you can anticipate that a slow device, such as a printer, may have wires coming *out* of it which can be used to shut off the computer's data flow. The obvious thing to do is to hook a printer's flow-control output to the computer's flow-control input.

However, if there is no flow control input wire on the computer, another flow-control method may possibly be used, or the data rate (baud rate) may just be set lower. In another case, if the computer has a flow-control input wire which you are not going to use, you will need to know how to deal with it. If left unconnected, such an input wire may prevent data from coming out of the computer.

The wires used for flow control are usually members of the group 4, 5, 6, or 20. As a general rule, if you have determined that your cable's data lines will be straight through (2-2 and 3-3) then, usually, the flow-control lines can be handled by wiring them straight through also (4-4, 5-5, 6-6, and 20-20). On the other hand, if you have decided on crossed data lines (2-3 and 3-2) then the usual way to cross the flow-control lines is as follows: 4-5 and 5-4, 6-20 and 20-6.

Again, these suggestions are frequently not the complete answer. Sometimes, other lines, such as 11 or 19, are used. You will need to look at the manuals to see what to do about these wires. If the manuals are ambiguous, you will have to use techniques presented in Chapter 8, 9 and 10.

Other Forms of Flow Control

Since I have just discussed hardware flow control, it is appropriate to complete that little picture by adding two common *software* flow-control methods. Both of these methods rely upon having two-way data communication (Pins 2 and 3 both used). Remember that there is a big difference between these methods. The hardware handshake methods change the states of certain wires for control, and use pins **other** than 2 or 3 for these functions. The software methods send characters for control, and hence use Pins 2 and 3 and **may not** need other signal lines.

XON-XOFF: This method is probably already familiar to you, but you may not realize it. Suppose you are sitting at your keyboard, and you get a directory or program listing on the screen. If the directory is a long one, it will go scrolling by and you'll miss the first part. On most systems, you can halt the flow by keying *Control-S*. This is, in fact, the XOFF character (also called DC3). To get the display started again, you can key *Control-Q* (although many systems permit any key to start the display when it is stopped). Control-Q is the XON character (also called DC1).

Similarly, a computer-and-printer system may be set up to use XON-XOFF. In this case, when the printer's buffer is full or paper runs out, the printer sends an XOFF (literally, a Control-S) to the computer. The computer, we hope, responds by shutting off the flow of characters until the printer sends it an XON.

ETX-ACK: This is a more complicated system, which can also be more sophisticated. Unfortunately, it is quite inconsistently implemented and, generally, is more trouble to get going than it is worth. It is easiest to get going when all equipment is from the same manufacturer. It is hardest to get going when the equipment is from different countries. Often, two devices claiming to do this sort of handshake turn out to be incompatible in this mode.

There is a general principle on which ETX-ACK operates. First of all, let us assume that we have a computer talking to a printer, although it might be two other devices. We'll also assume that they are operating correctly, so we'll just eavesdrop on the conversation.

The communication typically starts off with the sender equipment (e.g.: the computer) sending an ETX character (ASCII character 03, which is a Control-C). This is responded to by the receiver (e.g.: the printer) sending back an ACK (ASCII 06, Control-F), saying, "OK, go ahead." The sender then transmits a block of characters of maximum size which you have set to be the same at both equipments, let's say 128 characters. At the end of this string, the sender sends another ETX. When the receiver is ready, it replies with the ACK. The sender can now send another block of characters, and so it goes.

Different manufacturers implement this in all sorts of different ways. The block sizes may be different but can usually be set by switches or software. Also, the two characters may not be ETX and ACK. For example, Hewlett Packard plotters prefer ENQ (ASCII 05, Control-E) instead of ETX, but you may change it to any character you prefer.

Instead of using ETX-ACK for mere flow-control, other machines have schemes which allow you to actually correct errors. One such scheme involves *parity checking*. When the ETX is sent out, the receiver responds with ACK if everything is OK, and with *NAK* (ASCII 15 Hex, Control-U) if an error was detected. This response causes the transmitting unit to resend the faulty block.

Because of the variety of implementations. ETX-ACK is the *last* protocol you should opt for where possible.

Back to the Cable: The "Go-to-Sleep" Wire

There's a final class of RS-232X wire which you may encounter. This wire can cause you to tear your hair out if you don't expect it. It is an input, and its function is to cause the device to "go to sleep." If left unconnected it will signal go to sleep. Think about this. Here is a pin which will make a terminal (for example) unresponsive to totally legitimate data going *into* Pin 3!

This function *does* have a logical use. As an example, it can be used by a terminal-and-modem combination. Using Pin 8, the modem can signal to the terminal whether incoming (telephone-line) data is valid or not. This is useful because, when initially establishing a connection to the remote system, there may be noise on the phone line. The modem may interpret this as 1s and 0s and send them along Pin 3 to the terminal. The terminal may then display a few garbage characters on the screen. If Pin 8 is used, then the modem can also signal to the terminal that these are not valid data signals, preventing the garbage from appearing. Pin 8 is called Received Line Signal (RLSD) or Data Carrier Detect (DCD).

The use of a "go-to-sleep" pin seems to have lost favor with many equipment makers. This is probably due to the mysterious lack of operation which results if the appropriate signal is not supplied to it (resulting in bleating customers). But don't be surprised if you see it used. In certain cable diagrams later you will see it allowed for as a preventive measure.

Signal States on Flow-Control and Go-to-Sleep Wires

	Voltage	RS-232 Name	Control Meaning
Low	$-12V$	Mark	Not Ready
High	$+12V$	Space	Ready

Note: some equipment outputs, or requires as input, *inverted* control lines (High = Not Ready). This is obviously a problem. Before getting too upset, however, check the equipment manual to see if the sense of those lines can be inverted back to normal by flipping a switch or changing a jumper.

Unused Flow-Control and Go-to-Sleep Pins

There are a number of instances in which you or the equipment manufacturer don't want to use some of the signals which have just been discussed:

1. The first category concerns pins that may be unused by the manufacturer. This means that he either left the pins off the connector altogether or, if they are present, they perform no real function. If they are normally inputs, they go nowhere and influence nothing. If they are normally outputs, they may not be connected to anything internally, or the manufacturer may have thoughtfully connected them to a source of $+12$ volts. They can then signal "ready" to a possible input at the other end of the cable. This $+12$ volts is generally supplied through a resistor, so that if an accidental short occurs, the equipment's $+12$ volt power supply is not damaged.

2. The second category deals with output pins that may be unused by the reader. If you have an output pin which you don't need for flow control, then simply don't hook it up.

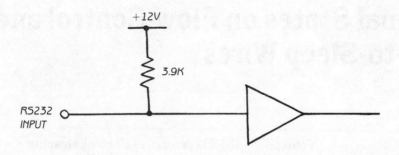

Figure 7-2 This illustrates adding a pull-up resistor to a sometimes unused flow-control or go-to-sleep input which can avoid headaches in the future.

3. The third category, which concerns unused *inputs*, is a bit more problematic. If your computer (for example) has a flow control input by which a printer can tell the computer to stop sending, there may be times when you don't need to use it. There is no problem if the input simply connects through the cable to a pin at the other end which is just pulled up to "ready." At other times you aren't so lucky. Can you just leave it unconnected? In older equipment, an unconnected input will often be interpreted as "stop." This also applies to the go-to-sleep type of inputs, which makes them especially annoying.

    On newer equipment, however, a pull-up resistor is connected *internally* to pull such input lines "high" or "ready." This is such an excellent idea that you may want to do this on equipment which doesn't have this built in. A 4 kilohm or so resistor from the signal line to +12 volts is all that is needed as in Figure 7-2. This is especially useful on equipment which gets plugged into many different systems on a frequent basis by non-expert users.

    We still have the cases where we may not want to modify the equipment, and we can't just wire the pin through the cable to it's companion at the other end, at least not with confidence. This problem may also be solved by some source of +12 volts—even +9 volts would do! We could take one of those small rectangular 9-volt batteries, hook its minus terminal to Pin 7, and use the +9-volt terminal to feed our input a "ready" signal.

    There is, of course, a simpler way. Let us suppose that the flow-control input is Pin 4. Then on the very same connector, Pin 5 usually provides a "ready" output! It is then sufficient to simply jumper Pin 4 to Pin 5! If Pin 5 is a *real* handshake output, then this jumper scheme will probably work. The occasions when Pin 5 indicates "not ready" probably will cause no problem. And of course, if Pin 5 is merely a dummy "ready" output, there would be no problem at all.

    This leads us to a couple of very useful cable arrangements.

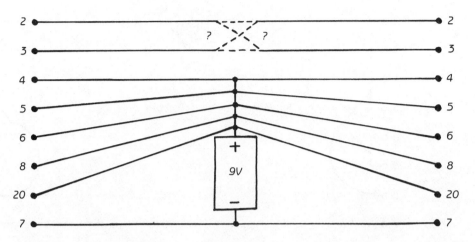

Figure 7-3   This is the Definitely-Sorta-Oughta-Work Cable. The battery sends all flow control inputs a "ready" signal.

Two Sorta-Oughta-Work Cables, Using No Hardware Flow Control

Armed with the knowledge discussed so far, we can arrive at a couple of cables which will almost always sort of work, because they eliminate all "problems" with hardware flow control and "go-to-sleep" inputs. Of course, in many situations, flow control is indeed needed for completely correct operation. The strategy here is to elicit at least some operation, and then use that to find out about the rest of the wires which may be needed. In particular, if there is any guesswork involved in getting the options set properly on each equipment (baud rate, number of bits, etc.), these cables will verify that you are getting close.

Once again, I remind you that the best way to proceed is to put together a test cable of the type already discussed. This is described fully in the next chapter, and makes the following experiments and tests quick and easy to perform.

The Definitely Sorta-Oughta-Work Cable: This one is the best hope to get something going as shown in Figure 7-3. You'll have to try 2 and 3 straight through or swapped (or set them according to the manuals). Other than that, we send a "ready" signal to all of the handshaking inputs that are commonly used. You might notice that we have indiscriminately connected many pins to +9 volts, some of which may be outputs. That's OK, RS-232 specifies that no damage will result from this, and our 9-volt battery can easily overpower any outputs which may try to be "low," thereby ensuring that all pins receive a "high."

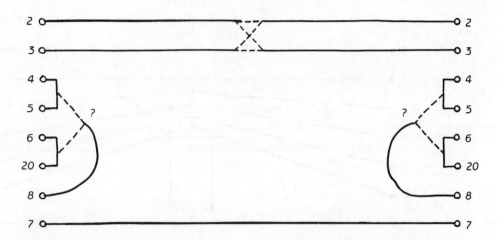

Figure 7-4   The Probably-Sorta-Oughta-Work Cable shown relies on somewhat conventional wiring at each end, and feeds usually "ready" outputs back into hungry inputs.

The Probably-Sorta-Oughta-Work Cable:

This cable, shown in Figure 7-4, works on the same principle, except that no battery is required. It relies on the very good chance that each equipments' own outputs can be used to satisfy their inputs. It is almost as good as the battery-powered method, but not quite so foolproof.

With this cable, you will have to decide whether or not to cross over the data wires 2 and 3. Pin 8 can be tried not connected, or jumpered to either 4-5 or 6-20.

XON-XOFF Stumbling Blocks:

Even after building one of these cables and obtaining some data communications, you will often still need to implement some kind of flow control. At this stage, you should have the data lines correctly wired. You would think that this would be the perfect opportunity to simply select XON-XOFF handshaking, and leave it at that (assuming both equipments have this capability). This might work, so try it!

In many situations, however, software or switch-setting ambiguities mess up the operation of the receiver-to-sender data line. In CP/M systems, for example, there is no standard way to handle data coming back from the printer device. Input and output in CP/M is handled by the Basic Input/Output System (BIOS). The BIOS obviously knows how to send data *out* to the printer, and usually knows to stop sending based on certain happenings on the hardware flow-control lines. On very few systems, however, does the BIOS know, by itself, how to do XON-XOFF handling.

You may think that perhaps an application program (MicroPro's *WordStar*, for example) will do the XON-XOFF handling. This doesn't provide flow control for Control-P printing using the TYPE command, but maybe we can put up with that. WordStar even let's us choose XON-XOFF in its configuration! Sorry, but it's just not that easy. CP/M systems are all so different. The only way to guide yourself through an installation such as this—and get it working—is if you already have the printer definitely working properly. You will also have to know quite a bit about the computer hardware and software—perhaps even to the point of writing an assembler-language driver routine. Yech!

XON-XOFF is not always that bad. However, it convinces us to continue our quest for hardware flow control to avoid these nightmares.

Adding Flow Control to Sorta-Oughta-Work Cables

If, as is frequently necessary, you decide to use hardware flow control, you often need it in only one direction. The following procedure outlines how to figure it out for one-way use. You can use the procedure twice if you need it both ways. In this procedure, we will assume that you are using the "Definitely Sorta-Oughta-Work" cable arrangement with the battery. In fact, let's go further and assume you have the more sophisticated setup using two batteries as shown in Figure 7-5. If you are using the "Probably" cable instead, you will have to modify the procedure, and be slightly more devious, but the idea is similar.

Budget Experimental Determination of Hardware Flow-Control Lines

Here I'll discuss some experimental techniques you can use. However, don't get depressed by how tedious the process appears. These first experiments are those which you can do with essentially no special equipment. In the next chapters, some very inexpensive test gadgets will be introduced which make these techniques much easier and quicker. The principles are the same, though, so read this section first.

Let us suppose that we are talking about a computer-and-printer setup. We've got it almost working with the Definitely Sorta-Oughta-Work cable. Data gets printed, but periodically the printer overflows. This is indicated by missing printout, or perhaps an error light. In any case, printers should *always* have flow control, because sooner or later they *will* overflow. I have chosen this example because everyone is familiar with this situation and knows what is supposed to happen. If you have a different situation, you can modify the procedure for your use.

You will need to determine two things:

1. which pin on the computer is the flow-control input

2. which pin on the printer is the flow-control output

(assuming these are suspected to exist).

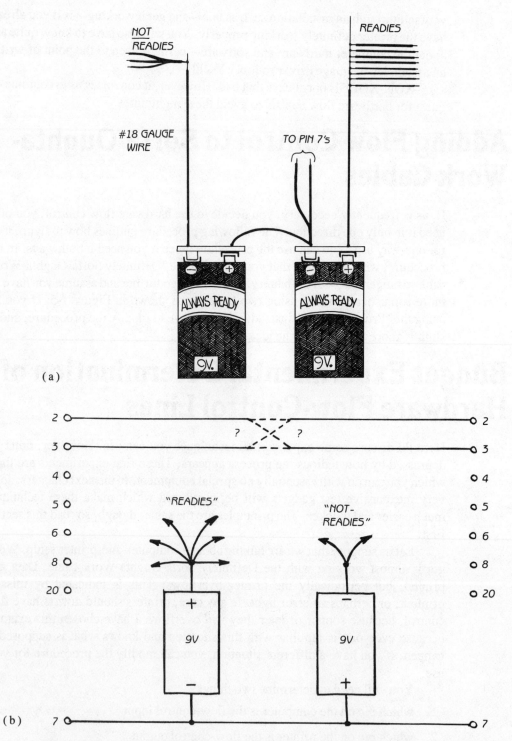

Figure 7-5   A pair of batteries provide the Ready and Not Ready signals which can be used in devising flow-control details.

The manual may have some information which will cut down on your "guessing and messing." When the manual is no help, it's time to experiment. First, we'll deal with the computer end. Begin by sending a long stream of characters from the computer to the printer and simultaneously to the screen, so you can see what's happening.

On an Apple, for example, do a PR # 1 command (2e's and 2c's require special attention at this point) and then LIST a long program. On a CP/M or MSDOS/PCDOS system, do a TYPE command on a long file with CTRL-P in effect. Or from MBASIC on any machine, set up a program, alternating PRINT and LPRINT in a loop. (And don't forget that, on many computers, the software controls which hardware handshake pins are operating!)

Flow-Control Input

First, we'll determine the computer's flow-control input. While the print out is happening, you will attempt to stop the action. By "stop," I don't mean that the printing will be stopped. The printer may continue to print from its internal buffer for some while. This is why I insisted on being able to see something happening on the screen. You may find a mirror helpful to view the screen—unless you have an assistant or can turn the monitor.

To stop the action, take each of the wires which is connected to the computer's possible flow-control pins (4,5,6,8,20), and, one by one disconnect it from the +9-volt battery providing the ready signal. Then, connect it instead to the −9 volt, not-ready signal from the other battery. (As you finish with each pin, reconnect it to the "ready" signal.) If hardware flow control is available and enabled by the computer's software, one or more of these wires will cause the screen action to stop! Don't forget which one, because you have found the flow-control input!

Flow-Control Output

Next, we'll determine which of the printer outputs is the handshake output. Begin by connecting up the Definitely-Sorta-Oughta-Work cable as before, but which now has the computer's flow-control input determined and separate. This should have a wire attached, ready to be connected temporarily to pins at the printer end. Again, get the computer to send out a stream of text. (At first, since the computer's flow-control input is not connected, attempting to get a printout may hang up the computer.)

Now, one by one, disconnect each of the suspected flow-control output pins on the printer end of the cable and connect it to the computer's flow-control input. I should mention that printers are notorious for using odd pins for flow-control outputs, so you may need to venture beyond the usual 4-5-6-8-20. You are watching for printing to continue or start, but this is not a sufficient clue, since this could happen with dummy ready outputs.

We need to find the printer's output which is normally "ready" but goes "not-ready" on certain conditions. So for each trial, force a "not-ready" condition by pushing the Off-line or Deselect button or by triggering the Out-of-paper sensor. With the correct pin hooked to the computer's flow-control input, this action should halt the screen activity, and you will have found the printer's flow-control output! (After each unsuccessful trial, reconnect each printer pin to the +9 volt "ready" signal in case it was an essential input).

Finishing the Cable

If you are using the "battery-assisted" Oughta-Work cable, you obviously will want to make another cable for the final installation which does not need batteries. The final step then, to finding the desired wiring will be to disconnect all the pins which continue to be supplied from the battery. If the setup no longer works, then you will have to search out those pins which need to be fed by the battery, and then replace the battery with jumpers to other pins which can supply the needed "ready" signals, in the style of the Probably-Sorta-Oughta-Work cable.

All Other RS-232 Wires

The above covers all of what I refer to as RS-232X. There are many more signals in the RS-232C definition, but these are so rarely used, (usually only in special modems) that you will need to get a proper explanation from the manual for their operation.

More Notes on Using a Trial Cable

By this time, you will have realized that simply trying out a cable arrangement to see if it works is a totally legitimate procedure. In general, you don't have to worry about mistakenly connecting two output wires together (a no-no in most electronics work). In RS-232, the circuitry is designed so as not to be damaged by connecting outputs together, or by shorting outputs to ground.

It is not too uncommon, however, to find that the equipment manufacturer has used some pins on the DB25 connector for some other, non-RS-232X purpose! One typical use is for a Centronics output or input (IDS Paper Tiger and Prism printers, for example). Another use is to provide connections for a *current-loop* interface. This is an older serial interface standard. If your manual mentions that you have pins used for those purposes, or other non-RS-232 functions, then **stay away from those pins** during experimentation, or circuit damage may result (usually not to the RS-232X circuitry, though!).

So, It Looks Pretty Tedious So Far...

There's no doubt about it. The procedures covered so far can lead to a rather long job, and many pieces of equipment do not lend themselves to the type of procedure we have just followed for the computer-printer case. Even in that case, you may not be able to achieve the very first level of "Sorta" communications.

Why not? The reason is easy to see. In bringing up an RS-232X connection for the first time, you are expecting many separate elements to be working correctly: software, switch settings, cable (and manual). What's worse, you can't test each element separately. You can't rely on a known-good cable with known-good Equipment A and known-good switch settings in order to get Equipment B set up correctly by trial-and-error.

What is needed is the ability to see what is going on in the system. You can then take corrective action based upon what is noticed. In fact, that is what we tried to do with the Sorta-Oughta-Work cable. We hoped that by making this basic cable, something would happen. Then, using the computer screen and the printer Deselect button as diagnostic tools, we tried to locate the flow-control wires. Often, however, the systems to be interconnected are not so cooperative as this in helping to diagnose what is going on.

The conclusion I am leading you to is this: it is well worth the effort to understand a little more about RS-232X, and to rig up some rudimentary monitoring equipment, to speed the job of interfacing.

The next chapter looks more deeply at what actually goes on in an RS-232X cable, and Chapter 9 introduces some simple gadgets you can put together to help you to see these activities (or lack of them!).

(KNIGHT "A")

DB-25s Through History.

(KNIGHT "B")

HERE WE SEE TWO KNIGHTS ENGAGED IN THE POPULAR PASTIME OF "EARS." EACH KNIGHT
TAKES A TURN SMACKING HIS DB25 AGAINST THE OTHER'S, IN AN EFFORT TO KNOCK IT'S
EARS OFF. IN THIS PICTURE, KNIGHT "B" HAS SUCCESSFULLY BEATEN KNIGHT "A." POINTS ARE
EARNED BY ADDING THE POINTS OF THE DEFEATED KNIGHT TO ONE'S OWN. BEFORE THIS
MATCH, KNIGHT "A" HAD 16 POINTS, AND KNIGHT "B" HAD 37. NOW, KNIGHT "B" HAS (37 + 16)
53 POINTS.

8

RS-232 Signals in Detail

In this chapter, we get more deeply into the specifics of what is happening on an RS-232X cable. You can draw upon this knowledge later in order to monitor the cable signals and understand what they mean and what to do about them.

The Data Line

The serial system uses only one wire to carry data. It does this by placing the bits, which make up each character, onto the wire one at a time in succession. A typical RS-232 signal looks like Figure 8-1. This is the picture which would appear if the data line was monitored on an oscilloscope.

Here are some of the salient features of Figure 8-1. First, note that the bits appear "least significant bit first." For those of you familiar with the ASCII code, the letter "A" is represented by decimal 65, which is hexadecimal 41, and 01000001 in binary. Thus the bits come out in the order 1-0-0-0-0-0-1-0. Next, you will notice that the 1s are represented by a − 12-volt level, and 0s by a + 12-volt level. Preceding the character is a bit called the *start* bit, and following the character

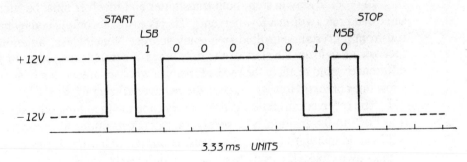

Figure 8-1 This illustrates an oscilloscope hooked to an RS-232 data wire showing the letter A at 300 baud. The data format is 8 bits and no parity.

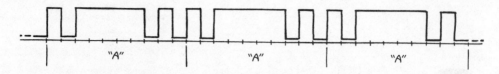

Figure 8-2 This is a sample of a string of "A"s, showing how they can be sent right next to each other.

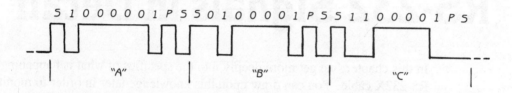

Figure 8-3 This is the string "ABC". The data format is 7 bits, with even parity.

comes the *stop* bit (I will explain their functions later). Before and after the letter A was sent, the voltage sits at −12 volts.

Each bit has been shown as occupying a 3.33 millisecond timeslot. This corresponds to 300 bits per second or 300 baud. Note that 300 baud, although defined as "300 bits per second", really means 3.33 milliseconds per bit, no matter how many bits were actually transmitted.

Figure 8-2 shows a continuous stream of data in progress, demonstrating that characters are right next to each other, with no space necessary between them. By now you may be wondering how the receiving end stays in step with the transmitter. After several hundred characters, how does the receiver know that the present 3.33 millisecond period is the second bit of the 376th character? This is a task which is aided by the start and stop bits, as we shall see.

In order to stay in step, both transmitter and receiver must be running at the same baud rate (within a few percent). This is easily accomplished by having each run from a crystal-controlled frequency source. Nonetheless, assuming that the receiver recognizes the start of the data when it commences, even a one-percent difference would result in the receiver being a whole character out of step after only a few lines of text! How, then, does the receiver correct for this?

The receiver correction is done every time the incoming data signal makes a 0-to-1 or 1-to-0 transition. The receiver expects transitions to occur only in 3.33-millisecond multiples (in this 300 baud example), at least as far as it can measure with its own clock. If a transition occurs a little early, this is an indication that the transmitter has got a little ahead, so the receiver jogs itself a little ahead also. Similarly, if a transition occurs late, the receiver slows itself down a little. With a normal string of text, transitions occur very frequently, and consequently, this corrective synchronization can keep the receiver in step very accurately.

What part do start and stop bits play? Suppose you send a string of characters composed of all 1s, or all 0s. Without the start and stop bits, there would be no transitions upon which to synchronize. The start and stop bits were added to ensure at least one transition per character. The start bit is always a high signal and the stop bit is always a low signal, so, at worst, there is always the transition between one character's stop bit and the next character's start bit.

7-Bit Codes: The ASCII code convention actually only covers 128 codes, which thus needs only 7 bits to represent them all. For this reason, many systems are set up for only 7-bit transmission and reception. Watch for the situation where a printer may work fine with either 7- or 8-bit communication for characters, but may require 8-bit operation in order to use dot-addressable graphics.

Parity: To finish the picture, Figure 8-3 shows the sequence of characters "ABC" with even parity added. Here I have shown 7-bit characters, as this is fairly common with mainframes communicating over phone lines where the error-checking virtue of parity comes in. *Even parity* is a scheme whereby an extra bit is added to the end of each character, the extra bit is either 0 or 1 to make the total number of 1s (lows) an even number. Similarly, *odd parity* is the scheme where an extra bit is added which makes the total number of 1s an odd number.

If any one of the character's bits gets mangled along the communications path, the receiving system (assuming that it's checking parity) will be able to detect the error when it adds up the 1s to see if the total is odd or even.

Note that you sometimes are given the choice of Mark or Space parity. This is not really parity at all. It is merely an extra bit of the stated polarity, filling in the spot where the parity bit would be. This is a convenient way to generate a character of the correct length for when the receiving equipment expects the extra bit, but ignores it.

Interaction Between Data Length and Parity

Note that certain combinations of character length and parity will look deceptively similar to other combinations, so far as the receiver is concerned. For example, in a computer-and-printer setup, suppose the computer sends characters as 7 bits plus parity (odd or even doesn't matter for this example). Now suppose the printer is expecting 8-bit codes where the lower 128 codes, (the last or *high-order* bit is 0), represent ordinary text characters, and the high 128 codes, (the high-order bit is 1), cause the printing of graphics characters. When the computer sends characters with a 0 parity bit, things look good. However, for those characters where the parity bit is 1, the perplexed user will see strange graphics materializing on the printer!

Needless to say, character length and parity selections can get you into trouble. Unfortunately, manuals are often fuzzy about the exact data format which each switch selection activates. You are frequently setting both transmit and receive parameters of your equipment with a single switch. If you set "ignore parity" this is clear with regards to reception, but ambiguous as to what characteristic this invokes in transmission.

As a consequence, you often have to try the most likely selections until you hit the right one. Selecting the number of stop bits is also sometimes a problem, but if you stick with one stop bit you are usually safe.

Some Equipment Is More Flexible than Others

While on the subject of character length and parity, it is useful to note that some equipment can handle the wrong data format, while others cannot. As an example, you might find that two different brands of terminal may be set to the same data format, but only one works in a particular situation. The other may not work at all, or work only partially. Later, it may be discovered that the data format selected was not what the remote system was using, but one of the terminals worked anyway. The conclusion is this: don't figure you've definitely hit upon the right format just because one piece of gear works.

Voltages and Input and Output Characteristics

I previously said that a high was +12 volts, and a low signal was −12 volts. In fact, the RS-232 standard specifies that RS-232 inputs are supposed to recognize the range at +3 volts to +15 volts as high, and −3 volts to −15 volts as low.

In RS-232X, the electronic components used to *drive* or transmit to the data or control lines, and to receive input from such lines, are very standard. Consequently, by noting the behavior of the driver and receiver components we can be pretty definite about what to expect in the way of signals, and their behavior in certain situations. It is not uncommon for standarization to occur more rapidly due to availability of such a standard component, as compared to the industry response to the edict of some committee.

The standard RS-232X transmitter integrated circuit is the 1488, also known as 75188. The standard receiver is the 1489, also known as 75189. A typical data or control line is shown in Figures 8-4 and 8-5.

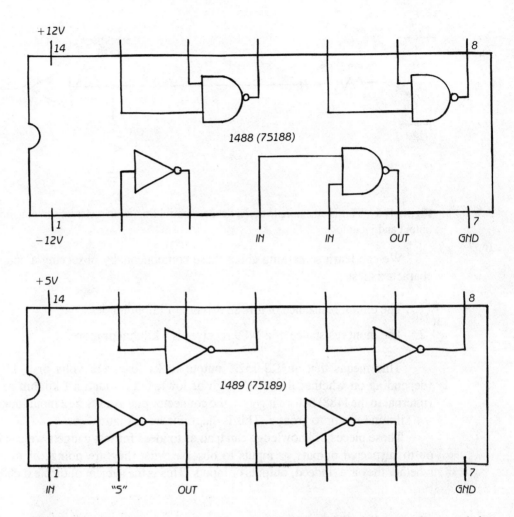

Figure 8-4   This depicts the internals of the 1488/75188 RS-232 transmitter, and the 1489/75189 receiver.

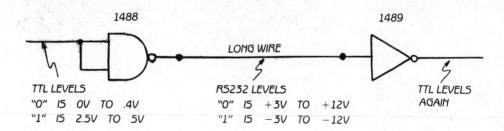

Figure 8-5   This shows a typical RS-232 data or control line.

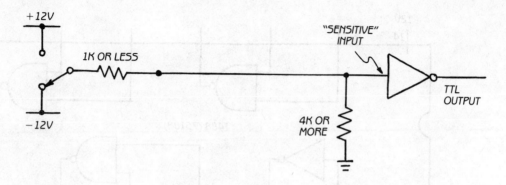

Figure 8-6   This is an example of the data or control line, with resistors showing how the output and input look.

We can learn something about these components by observing a couple of characteristics:

1. The output resistance of a 1488 driver is 1 kilohm or less.

2. The input resistance of a 1489 receiver is 4 kilohm or more.

This means that an RS-232X output looks like +12 volts or −12 volts (depending on whether the state's high or low), fed through a 1 kilohm resistor (internal to the 1488) before it gets to the connector pin. An RS-232 input looks like a 4-kilohm resistor to ground. This is diagrammed in Figure 8-6.

These pieces of knowledge can lead us to ideas for test gadgets we can hook on to suspected outputs or inputs to observe what they are doing, or to check whether they are, indeed, outputs or inputs. This is the subject of the next chapter.

Breakout Bots in action!

Breakout Boxes in action!

9

Test and Monitoring Gadgets

In this chapter, I will show how to construct a trial cable and a collection of signal-monitoring gadgets. You will notice that the gadgets progress from simple to fairly complex, but each step in sophistication is an embellishment on the previous design.

The Trial Cable

This is merely a device which allows you to test cable ideas quickly and easily, with a minimum of frustration. It is made entirely of 25-wire ribbon cable, and "squash-on" (IDC) DB-25 connectors, available at the local "Shack" or elsewhere. See Chapter 11 on RS-232X Hardware for details on connectors, purchasing and assembly.

The cable pictured in Figure 9-1 may be thought of as a single 8- or 10-foot length of ribbon, with both male and female connectors at *each* end, ensuring that the appropriate sex will be available. At some point, the cable is cut across, making two separate cables. On each side of this cut, a female DB-25 is attached. These two connectors are fastened to a piece of metal or wood to hold them conveniently close together. The two female connectors provide contacts which can be jumpered together to make any configuration of cable desired. Often, the connectors have numbers molded next to each hole! The jumpers can simply be short lengths of solid #18 wire (insulated, with ends stripped), or they can be real DB-25 male pins, if some can be obtained.

This setup requires only the squashing of the 6 connectors and the securing of the center pair. In 15 minutes, you can start getting to work! (Don't forget to install the connectors the right way around!!)

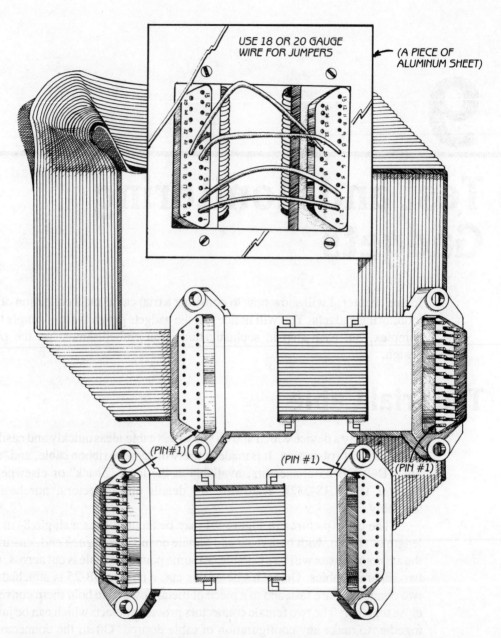

USE 18 OR 20 GAUGE
WIRE FOR JUMPERS

(A PIECE OF
ALUMINUM SHEET)

(PIN #1)

(PIN #1)

(PIN #1)

Figure 9-1   The basic RS-232X Trial Cable is a must for any serious sleuthing.

You may wish to add clips for attaching a couple of 9-volt batteries for test purposes. You can also make up some jumpers which let you connect multiple holes together or to the batteries. Then again, you might prefer to read on and see what else you can add to this gadget!

The Philosophy of Monitoring Gadgets

Next, we turn our attention to being able to *see* what is happening on an RS-232X wire. If you are already equipped with a voltmeter or oscilloscope, you can try using those. However, digital voltmeters don't indicate important short pulses, and oscilloscopes are too bulky and must be plugged in to wall sockets. Old-style, analog-needle meters can come in handy but are still not ideal.

I am not going to present a lot of specific procedures surrounding the use of such monitors. The intent of these monitors is to test for the presence or absence of data activity, or a readiness state. With those pieces of information, the reader should be able to determine which piece of equipment is causing the problem, and work from there, following procedures based upon the preceding chapters. As a further trick, I will show how to test an unknown RS-232X interface to determine which of its pins are inputs, which are outputs and which pins are unconnected.

What Indications Would We Like?

Type A Indicator: At the very least, we need some indication of the high or low signals which may be present on a wire. A light, perhaps an LED, would suffice as an indicator. We would expect this light to pulse in response to a flow of data. This would be our Type A indicator.

Type B Indicator: We would like a similar indicator arrangement to signal a short burst of pulsing activity, as might result if an XOFF was sent. At high data rates, this might be invisible on our Type A indicator. At 9600 baud, each bit takes only about a ten-thousandth of a second!

The indicators and gadgets which follow satisfy these two needs.

The Primitive Indicator

This indicator is diagrammed in Figure 9-2. It consists of just 3 components, costing perhaps a dollar. It is referred to as a *line-powered indicator*, because the power for the light-emitting diode comes from the RS-232 line. The LED will not be terribly bright, but it is better than nothing. Use a small, red LED for best results.

In the diagram, one end of the test indicator is labeled as plus, and the other end is minus. If you hook the minus end to ground (Pin 7) and the plus end to an RS-232X line, the LED will glow if the line is high or positive. This is the best orientation for looking at data lines. If, instead, the plus end is grounded, and the minus end is attached to the signal, the LED will glow on lows. This is the best orientation for looking at flow control, where the LED glows on "Not Ready."

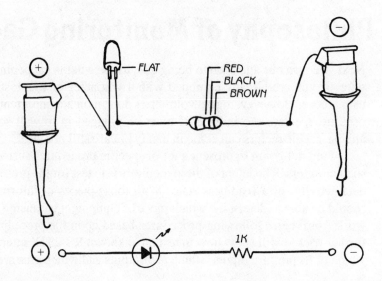

Figure 9-2 One LED, one resistor and a couple of clips are all it takes to make a primitive RS-232 test monitor.

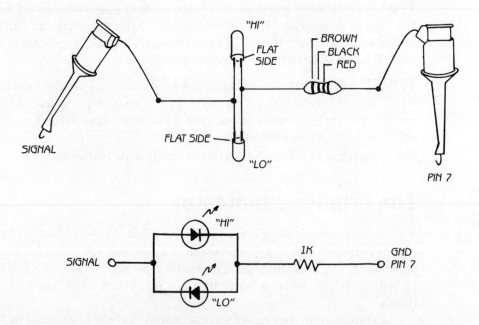

Figure 9-3 Here's the luxury primitive monitor, for the additional price of one LED.

You have to be a little cautious in using this kind of indicator, because it "loads down" the RS-232 signal. That is to say, if the data line had a healthy +12 volt and −12 volt swing, the half of the swing which makes the LED glow will be "loaded down" to perhaps +6 volts or −6 volts. So, if your communications link suddenly works differently when you attach your "monitor," you will know why.

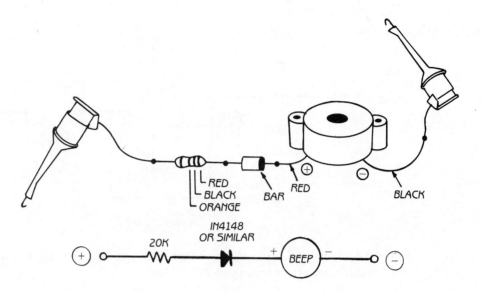

Figure 9-4   The audio version of the simple test monitor is better if you don't want to "load down" the RS-232 line, and also for catching quick pulses.

A Double-Ended Primitive Monitor

This is exactly the same as the previous indicator, except that it includes two LEDs, one for highs and one for lows. You don't have to keep switching it around for different signals, but can just leave one end grounded, as shown in Figure 9-3.

The same caution applies to this indicator in regards to loading. Also, if you are tempted to use LEDs which are not red, bear in mind that these are much dimmer with the limited amount of current available from the RS-232 line.

Beeper

The tester shown in Figure 9-4 has a couple of unique qualities. First of all, it uses what is known as a *Piezoelectric element*, which is simply a very efficient beeper which draws very little power. This presents only a small load to the line being monitored, reducing the likelihood of disturbance. Secondly, our ears are much quicker than our eyes. Therefore, with the beeper, we have a chance of catching the short, quick pulsing of a 9600-baud XOFF. The diode can be any silicon signal diode, such as 1N4148 or 1N914 or any of about a million others.

This monitor also has a plus and minus end. With the minus end grounded, the beeper will beep on a positive pulse (good for data lines). The opposite is true when the plus end is grounded.

There is no point of course, in making a double-ended beeper, since you wouldn't be able to tell which beeper was beeping. (Well, you *could* make a pair of headphone-style beepers, and listen in stereo...)

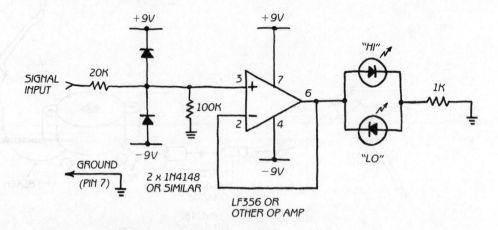

Figure 9-5   With a little extra effort, you can make a sensitive monitor which gives you LED indicators and avoids loading the RS-232 line.

Buffered Monitor

For a few extra dollars, you can alleviate the potential loading problems of the Primitive Double-Ended Monitor, while turning it into a more sensitive instrument capable of some other tricks. This is pictured in Figure 9-5.

This monitor uses an op-amp integrated circuit amplifier (available at electronics stores) to sense the RS-232X signal, and to provide the power to light the LEDs. The op-amp requires a plus and minus supply, which is provided by a pair of 9-volt batteries. The power for the LEDs also comes from the batteries via the op-amp. You can also use a pair of 12-volt batteries if you wish, or even build a plus-and-minus 12-volt power supply.

This monitor is so sensitive that it presents essentially no load to the RS-232X line that it is monitoring. It is this characteristic which we need for the next technique.

Figuring Inputs and Outputs with No Documentation

Sooner or later, you come across some equipment where there is either no book, or you're sure the book is wrong. With the gadget described here, you will be able to take a totally unknown RS-232X interface and determine which pins are not connected internally, which pins are inputs and which are outputs.

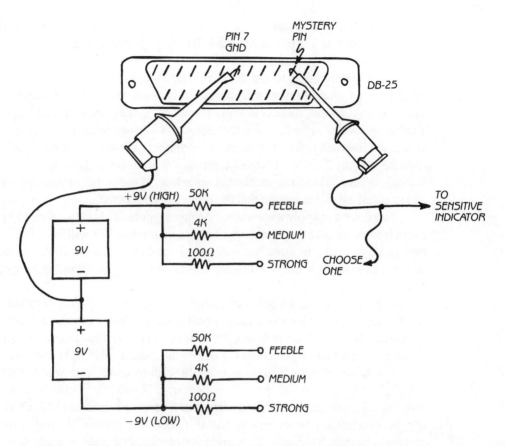

Figure 9-6   This illustrates the basic technique for sniffing out mystery pins.

Simple Pin Sniffer

In the following discussion, I am going to examine a single mystery pin in a mystery RS-232X interface. The procedure is to hook up our sensitive, Buffered Monitor, then apply certain external signals to that pin, and see what result is indicated on the Monitor. This is pictured in Figure 9-6.

First, switch on the mystery equipment, so that whatever signals and levels there might be on the mystery interface connector will be exhibiting their normal behavior. Hook up just the monitor to the mystery pin (and ground, of course).

Immediately, our monitor will give us some clues. If the lights are off, then the pin we have is either not connected, ground, or an input. If the high LED indicator is on, then the pin is either an output, or pulled high as in a dummy output or a pulled-high input. Similarly, if the low LED indicator is on, that pin is probably either an output, or permanently wired low.

Note that it is possible that if your sensitive monitor is attached to an internally unconnected pin, then both LEDs may glow dimly, because it is sensitive enough to pick up AC hum.

Next, we are going to attach a feeble signal to this mystery pin. If the pin can be influenced, our Monitor will indicate a change. We can then be certain that, inside the equipment, there is nothing connected to that pin. Our first feeble signal can be +9 volts or +12 volts through a 50 kilohm resistor. If the pin is not connected internally, this will cause our monitor, first indicating no signal, to now indicate a high. Next we connect instead −9 volts (or −12 volts) through a 50 kilohm resistor. This time we should see a low. If these indications appeared, we can stop testing and conclude that the pin is not connected.

Next, we can apply a somewhat stronger signal. This signal should be strong enough to cause an *input* to change, but not an *output*. We will be using the same two voltages, but this time we will use 4 kilohm resistors. If these cause our monitor to give high and low readings, then the pin is an input, and we can stop testing.

After these tests, the only remaining possibilities for the mystery pin are that it is an output, or that it is permanently pulled high or low, or to ground. If the pin is grounded, neither of our indicators will have lit so far. The other alternatives are characterised by having caused only one of the indicators to light and stay lit.

If you are curious further, you might wish to investigate whether the pin is wired directly to some voltage source, perhaps a 12 volt power output (unusual, but possible). It may also be an output driver or a resistor connected high or low. This can be determined by repeating the test, but this time with very low-valued resistors, such as 100 ohms. The direct connection to a power-supply voltage will not yield to this external influence, while the other possibilities will. Remember that a 1488 driver looks like plus or minus 12 volts fed through a 1 kilohm resistor.

Swifter Sniffer

The above series of tests looks tedious, but can be carried out quite quickly. However, to further speed the process, there is a gadget which *automatically* switches you between high and low test signals. Figure 9-7 shows a slow oscillator, providing a sequence of highs and lows. The output of the oscillator is connected to the three resistor values needed for sniffing.

The above test sequence is modified in that you only need to connect the mystery pin to half as many test-signal sources, and the highs and lows are provided for you.

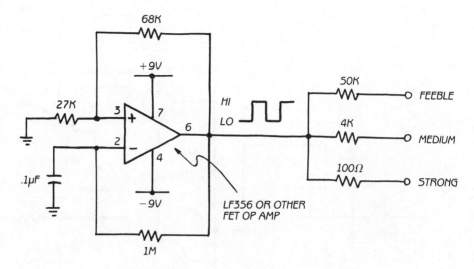

Figure 9-7   A simple, slow oscillator automatically flips between high and low signals.

The Sophisticated Monitor

Figure 9-8 shows a further embellishment of the Buffered Monitor. The enhancement involves the addition of two more LEDs and associated circuitry. This is intended to catch short, positive and negative pulses, and to stretch the LED pulse to about a second. In this way, infrequent, high baud-rate activity can be seen. This same activity can be heard on a beeper as a click, but you may prefer a visual indication instead.

Construction of this tester is probably not a "first project," but if you have the experience and knowledge to follow the schematic, then you should have little difficulty in putting it together.

Use of an Oscilloscope

If you are accustomed to using an oscilloscope, it may seem peculiar that I have avoided mentioning the scope as a useful test instrument. In fact, this is quite intentional. From my experience, I have concluded that the scope is rarely the best instrument for an RS-232 job.

First of all, even most of the portable scopes are rather heavy to lug around, and must be plugged in to a power outlet. Even if this is not an inconvenience to

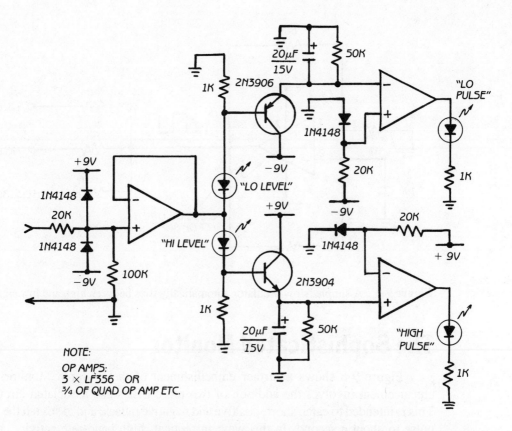

Figure 9-8   This sophisticated monitor not only shows the immediate state of the wire under observation, it also captures quick pulses and displays them over a stretched time period.

you, it turns out that RS-232 signals are not particularly well suited to observation on a scope, for reasons elaborated below.

To obtain a stable display on a scope, you need a signal which repeats at a regular and fairly rapid interval. You also need a once-per-cycle distinctive feature for the scope to trigger upon. RS-232 data signals provide neither of these features, being particularly difficult at low baud rates, and with low character rates.

Undeniably, a scope can sometimes offer you insight into what's happening on an RS-232 data line. If you want to get an idea of the baud rate at which transmission is occuring, you can look at a scope trace and observe the time occupied for one bit. If you can transmit a string of the letter U, this makes things easier. The letter U is 01010101 in binary, providing a square wave display whose bit times are easy to measure. Don't forget that there may be 7 or 8 data bits, a parity bit, and start and stop bits. If you know what the format of the data is, then you can pick out these features in a scope trace. However, if you *don't* know the format, it is surprisingly difficult to figure it out from the scope. This is why it is easier to try to match data formats by educated trial and error. Even the modem jitter mentioned in the next chapter is only barely observable with a scope.

Tricks.

10

Miscellaneous Tricks, Hints, and Bizarrities

Gathered herein is a "potluck" of notes on all sorts of items. Some notes are specific to certain popular machines, but all have value beyond their particular situations. This is my attempt to bring to you some "instant experience." I hope to broaden your RS-232X knowledge so that your thought processes will be flexible enough to expect the strange, and give you the confidence to tackle it.

These items are grouped in general themes.

Computers Which Don't Use DB-25 Connectors

You may have noticed that the techniques for testing RS-232X signals work wonderfully, so long as you have a ground wire to start from. With DB-25 RS-232 connectors you can be confident that Pin 7 will be ground, but what do you do with machines which use some other connector?

If all you need is to find the ground, then usually you can get the information from the manual. Or perhaps a cable has been provided that has a DB-25 on one end, from which an ohmmeter or battery-and-lamp continuity tester will tell you where Pin 7 comes out on the non-DB-25 end.

At the very worst, you can try to find the connector pin which has conductivity to some other known ground point. (Use only an ohmmeter for this test to avoid damage to components.) One convenient point which is generally grounded is the outer contact of the video connector, if an RCA phono jack is used. Otherwise, you can use a ground pin on a logic chip.

It is quite likely that an increasing number of computers will be manufactured with smaller RS-232 connectors, due to the lack of panel space, and obvious wasted expense. These connectors may be DB-9s, as on Macintoshes, DECmates, PC-ATs, and Atari STs, or DIN connectors as on some Radio Shack products. Once again, no book can be completely up to the minute, or attempt to provide information on all machines, but with the techniques already provided, that sort of information is unnecessary. Therefore, I am presenting here just a few sample cases.

Apple Macintosh

I am including a special note on the *Mac* because the MacSerial Port is rather different, and could cause bewilderment. The first thing to notice is that the Mac uses a DB-9 connector for each of its two serial ports, so we must expect a bit of a rethink.

A MacSerial port is more than just an RS-232X port. It also can carry on conversations in a convention called RS-422 (yep, they've been at it again). RS-422 can operate a great deal faster than RS-232, but to do so it uses a convention called *differential signals*. This means that each signal uses two wires, one for the "normal" signal, and one for its inverse. When one wire is indicating +12 volts, its partner is at −12 volts.

At the receiving end, a receiver chip simply compares the incoming pair of wires to each other. If the normal wire is higher than the inverse wire, then the receiver chip sees high. If the normal is lower than the inverse, the result is a low. This scheme can operate faster than the single wire RS-232 system, and is much less prone to electrical noise, since any noise will affect both wires of the pair equally.

So how do you hook up RS-232X to the Macintosh? First, take a look at the MacConnector diagram in Figure 10-1. Notice the two transmit-data lines and the two receive-data lines. Imagine testing for those with our normal techniques. Not knowing about the RS-422 inverted data lines, you might have some surprises!

Along with the two pairs of data lines, there is another input line, which apparently can he used for various different purposes, depending on the software. In any case, terminal software can use this input for a Data Carrier Detect signal, which makes this a "go-to-sleep" input, again depending on software.

Figure 10-2 provides some samples of the kinds of cable which can be used in certain Mac applications. The main uses for the serial ports at present are for use with the Imagewriter printer, or with a modem, and for both of these, cables are available. If you want to use non-Apple printers or modems, the information here will be of some help. But the usefulness of non-Apple printers is limited by the lack of software to support their special features.

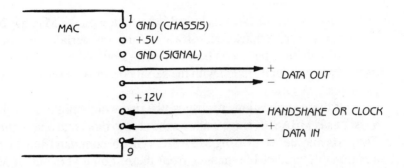

Figure 10-1   The Macintosh's serial port is shown here.

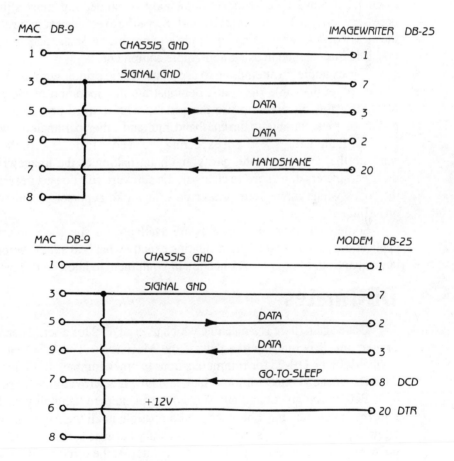

Figure 10-2   Samples of cables used with the Mac.

Also, since little, real technical information on the Mac has been released to the general user, application software using the serial port must generally be supplied with information on how to wire or obtain the appropriate cables. Users, themselves, cannot do much with the serial port outside the control of applications packages.

Of these applications packages, the one which might draw the most curious questions is MBASIC, since it allows the user to input and output through the ports. The ports may be set up using MBASIC's OPEN command and the port operates in a reasonably predictable manner from there. Some versions of Mac's ROMs or MBASIC may not be as versatile as others about sending XOFF to the remote machine when Mac's input buffer gets full.

As a final note on the Mac, it should probably be mentioned that Mac is no different from other computers when you attempt to hook up a serial device (for example, a non-Apple printer). Somebody or something must still do all the necessary jobs relating to the serial port. Since the average user is "protected" from the messy details when using all-Apple equipment, he or she may not be aware of the problems entailed in using non-Apple equipment.

For example, in attempting to use a non-Apple printer with the Mac, the first step is to get the cable right, and demonstrate the operation of the printer from MBASIC. But, in order to use the printer with a word-processor, that word-processor must be able to set the baud rate and other parameters, which, in all likelihood, the authors were not expecting you needed to do. Even if the printer will run with the same baud rate, parity and handshaking as the Imagewriter (so that these parameters don't need to change), the software still doesn't necessarily know the codes which make your printer do things like superscript and subscript, or underline.

Some cable-plus-software kits are available for specific printers and other applications, and it is worth investigating exactly what is available before spending large quantities of cash on a collection of equipment to hook on to Mac.

DECmates

Once again, here is a machine which uses a DB-9 for a serial connector to the printer, but it is quite unlike that of the Macintosh. The DECmate also has a normal-looking DB-25 for communications to other computers. Figure 10-3 shows what DECmate's connector looks like, and how it is wired to DEC printers.

Before you go out and buy some other printers to hang on your DECmates, remember that they must be software-compatible in all their special codes, or the effort is pointless. This is especially necessary because some DEC software starts up by requesting a status report from the printer. If the printer cannot respond, the software thinks that there is no printer. Unfortunately, I have yet to see a non-DEC printer which can respond to these codes.

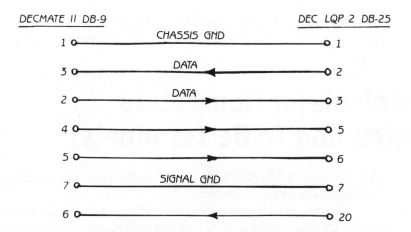

Figure 10-3   How the DECmate II connects to the Letter Quality Printer.

While on the subject of DECmates and DEC word processors in general, a couple of notes are in order. First, while other printers cannot be made to work satisfactorily on DEC word processors, DEC's printers will work with other personal computers. However, they generally expect to do XON/XOFF handshaking, which may be problematic, depending on your computer and software. Some IBM PCs and compatibles will handle this nicely. We have also run DEC printers from a KayPro, however it required writing an assembler language driver routine, which, on that machine, is not easy to install.

There may also be some interest in transferring files from DEC word processors (or indeed other brands) to other machines, particularly to popular personal computers. This is *not* merely "putting it on a different disk format." First of all, to my knowledge, there is no convenient way to transfer such files disk-to-disk. This is largely because most DEC word processors are based on a PDP-8 and its ancient conventions, and use an inconvenient disk format. For example, the DECmates with 5.25-inch floppy disks use single-sided, 96 track-per-inch drives, which are not standard equipment on any popular personal computer.

However, DEC's word-processing software *does* come with a communications option which allows sending files via RS-232 to another machine. The file can be communicated in two different formats. One format (DX) retains all of the formatting (width, justification, paging, underlines, etc.) for sending to a similar DEC machine, running similar software. The other format (CX) drops all of the format information and allows the file to be sent to almost any other system. It is for the user to decide if the file is of much use, now that all of the formatting has been stripped out.

There are a limited number of software packages which claim to be able to make the transfer *and* do a translation into the code system of another word processor, for example, from a DEC word processor to MicroPro WordStar. If you are interested in this type of transfer, then you should contact your word-processor vendor, or scour magazines aimed at users of the word-processor system you have.

Terminals (or Computers Pretending To Be Terminals)

If you are having a tough time with a terminal, here are a few quick tests which may help you track down the problem.

The principal, no-instruments way of testing a terminal is using the *loop-back* technique. Since a terminal can both send and receive, we can arrange ways to have its output monitored by its input. This helps us to get wiring correct, and to figure out whatever handshaking requirements are needed by the terminal.

1. The first step is to see if the terminal is alive by putting it in *local* mode, that is, off line. In this mode, regardless of the connector wiring, what you type at the keyboard should appear on the screen. If not, there must be an internal defect.

2. Next, put the terminal "on-line." Remove the cable from the terminal to the modem or remote system, if that has been attached. Try typing on the keyboard now. If characters appear, mentally note that the terminal must be in half-duplex (local-echo) mode, and that it also apparently requires no special satisfaction of handshaking inputs.

3. Next, jumper Pins 2 and 3 together (using a paper clip for a female plug) on the terminal's RS-232X connector. Typing on the keyboard now should send characters out, which come right back in and appear on the screen. If the terminal demonstrated that it was in half duplex in Step 2, then you should see doubled characters now.

If nothing appears at this stage, then it must be a flow-control line problem, either prohibiting data from coming out (most likely on computers), or a go-to-sleep problem (in both terminals or computers). We can be 99 percent certain that at least the baud rate, parity and number of bits are set compatibly (for itself). So, use the battery trick to pull up each possible flow-control line (4, 5, 6, 8, 20) or jumper the lines together (4-5, 6-20-8). Something should happen now, otherwise you have a hardware defect, an extremely strange terminal, or, on a computer, perhaps your software is not using the correct serial port.

4. If you get some action at this last point, you can continue expanding the "loop" of the loopback test. You can now connect on the cable you were proposing to use, and loopback the remote end of the cable. After that, if you are using a

modem, you may find that the modem has a half-duplex setting which will work as a loopback test (you may need to be online for this to operate). Get the idea?

If the terminal passes various levels of the loopback test, but refuses to communicate with the remote computer system, then this isolates the problem to wrong baud, parity or number of bits. Occasionally, you may even encounter an old terminal whose baud rate appears to be set correctly, but which has drifted off a few percent. This is quite unlikely with newer terminals whose rates are crystal-controlled.

ESCape Sequences

You don't have to use a terminal very long before you run into the mysteries of *escape sequences*. First of all, Escape is a character, represented by the ASCII code 27 (decimal) which is the same as hexadecimal 1B, or binary 00011011. It is sometimes used by itself, and most terminal keyboards have an ESC key for this purpose. However, by far the most frequent job for ESC is as the lead-in character in a two- to five-character, special-function sequence.

Most terminals are preprogrammed by the manufacturer to recognize certain sequences of characters from the computer (beginning with ESC) as a command to perform a special function. Examples of these functions are: direct positioning of the cursor to a certain location on the screen, deleting characters to the end of line or screen, changing the appearance of subsequent characters to "reverse video," underline or high intensity, and so on. In a similar fashion, if the terminal has keys which do not have standard ASCII codes (such as function keys, arrow keys, etc.), these may be transmitted by the terminal to the computer as ESCape sequences also.

As you might have expected, there is not just one standard determining which ESCape sequences mean what. Instead, there are a number of conventions. These essentially amount to groups of manufacturers making new terminals which behave like one or another of the "original" terminals which used ESCape sequences. You will see a terminal claiming to "emulate a DEC VT52" or "emulate a Hazeltine" etc. Naturally, it will be important that your software know what kind of terminal it is talking to, if it is to perform any of these intelligent-screen maneuvers. If the software is set up for the wrong terminal, the ESCape sequences sent out will mystify your terminal and you.

Actually, there *is* an American National Standards Institute (ANSI) standard ESCape sequence set, but manufacturers have been slow to adopt it. This may be because it is rather more complicated than the proprietary sequences (although it is quite comprehensive). This standard is used in the DEC VT100 terminal, and hence the terms "VT100 compatible" and "ANSI-standard compatible" are used almost interchangeably.

"Break"

On most computer systems, some means is provided to "interrupt" the computer and call its attention the operator. On some systems and many personal computers, this is done with a Control-C. However there is also a widely used convention which uses a system called *Break*. On the terminal keyboard, there is a Break key which looks just like any other key. However, unlike other keys, it does **not** send a character to the remote system, although it does cause an action on the terminal's outgoing data line.

When you hit the Break key, this causes a special action to occur. The data output line, which normally sits low at the Mark state, is raised high to the Space signal level, for a duration of perhaps a second. Note that this is a very unusual thing for the data line, which normally carries data in strings of pulses! Nonetheless, this "long space" is a convention on some systems.

On some personal computers it is difficult to generate a Break properly. Normally a computer's RS-232X port is internally controlled by a chip called a UART (Universal Asynchronous Receiver-Transmitter), and it may be difficult or impossible to program the chip to generate a Break condition. Watch for this if you are in the process of getting computers with terminal software for use with mainframes needing Break.

Autobauding

In systems which consist of a computer directly wired to one or more terminals, a feature called *autobaud* may be used. This means that, instead of having to set switches inside the computer or run some configuration software, the computer looks at the data coming from the terminal and sets itself to the correct baud rate automatically.

Generally, a strict procedure must be followed. For example, when the terminal is powered up, you may have to hit 4 or 5 Carriage Returns. This gives the computer a chance to "lock on" to a consistent series of known characters. Some machines are decidedly better than others at autobauding. If you key something else, some machines will get mixed up and *never* be able to autobaud until the computer is reset.

How does autobauding work? Essentially, the computer sets up the UART chip which is controlling your RS-232 port at a certain baud rate. Then the computer keeps checking the chip to see if any characters came in, and if any errors occurred. The UART is pretty smart and can indicate an error if it receives what it considers is mangled data. If no error occurred, and a Carriage Return came in, the baud rate is right! However, if an error occurred or the wrong character came in, then the computer tries setting the UART to a different baud rate. A wrong character with no error is still considered to indicate a wrong baud rate, since it is quite possible for data pulses at one rate to look like some other character of another rate.

The process continues until the right baud rate is found. But there are problems. This method cannot seek out the correct data format (number of bits, parity, and stop bits), because some data formats look like others, for certain sets of characters. Also, if the terminal is initially set to a format which causes an error in the UART even at the correct baud rate, then the autobaud operation will fail.

So, autobauding is far from foolproof, and still requires messing around to get it going.

Listening In with a Printer or Plotter

Here is a method you can use to operate a local printer or plotter if you are using a terminal with a remote time-share system. Looking at Figure 10-4, you can see that, essentially, the printer is "listening in" on what the remote system is sending to the terminal. Remember that in most time-share systems full-duplex operation is used, which means that the printer will be listening to everything which appears on the terminal's screen.

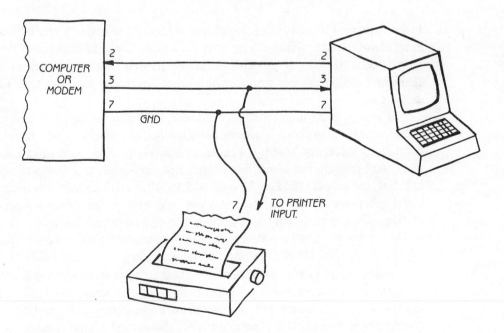

Figure 10-4   This illustrates a handy technique for obtaining hardcopy output on printer or plotter when the computer does not provide a convenient printer or plotter output. The printer listens in to the data *from* the computer.

You may be a little worried about buffer overflow, and the inability of the printer to control the flow from the remote system. First, most dot-matrix printers will run quite well at the 300 baud (about 30 characters per second) which is commonly used. There is more likely to be a problem at 1200 baud however, and there will certainly be a problem if higher speed, direct-communications lines are used between terminal and remote computer.

One solution is to make sure the printer has a large buffer (say 4-K characters), then control the flow using XOFFs (Control-S) from the terminal keyboard. This method is tedious at best.

If the printer will do XON-XOFF flow control, then there is an alternative solution. First of all, you cannot simply wire together the terminal's data output and the printer's data output. Although no damage will result, the two connected outputs will not produce meaningful RS-232X signals. What is needed is to combine the two data output signals in some other manner, so that, if either one attempts to send data, proper RS-232X signals result. This can usually be done, thanks to the almost-universal use of the trusty 1488, and its lucky features. This is diagrammed in Figure 10-5. Note that it will still be illegal for the two outputs to attempt to transmit simultaneously. However, this is unlikely to happen, and in any case is not catastrophic.

Printer ESCape Sequences

Just as with terminals, printers are also programmed to perform special functions in response to particular codes or code sequences. Some of the special functions may be activated simply by using otherwise-unused characters (such as control characters which do not print), while other functions may use true ESCape sequences.

There is even less agreement on code-sequence meanings among printer manufacturers than there is among terminal manufacturers. There have been a number of instances where a printer was advertised to perform all sorts of wonderful printing functions, like superscript, subscript, and proportional spacing. Yet, the printer could not be used with word-processing software because the codes necessary for that printer were not programmed into the word-processor routines. Customers buying such printers can only hope that the particular printer would become popular enough that a future version of the word-processor program might include that printer in its installation menu. Printer buyers, beware!

Fortunately, printer manufacturers seem to have recognized this problem, and generally make their new printers emulate popular older models. This means that daisy-wheel printers with word-processing functions will emulate a letter-quality printers like Diablo, Qume, or NEC. Newer dot-matrix printers may also emulate one of these printers when doing correspondence-quality printing, and then emulate a long-time favorite dot-matrix printer when doing dot-addressable graphics.

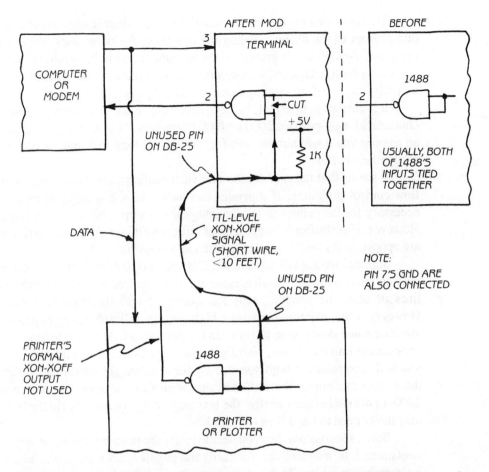

Figure 10-5 In many listening-in applications, it would be necessary either to run at a low baud rate, or to implement flow-control. Shown here is a convenient way to modify the equipment to perform XON-XOFF flow-control.

Thus, although it is possible to get almost any printer to run in simple teletype-like fashion, it is necessary to ensure that the software knows how to run the printer's fancy features if the most utility is to be obtained from the system.

Printer Buffers

The following is a note on serial interfaces with built-in buffers. It is a cautionary note for printer purchasers and cablers.

It is common that when a printer is supplied with a serial RS-232 interface, it also comes with a built-in buffer. Almost all printers (serial or parallel) can buffer a linefull of characters, because it makes printing more efficient. But the buffers I am describing are capable of receiving several thousand characters at a fast rate. The buffer stores the characters while they await being printed by the relatively slower print mechanism.

This arrangement appears to benefit the user, since it allows text to be quickly dumped out to the buffer, freeing the computer for other uses while printing is going on. This benefit is greatest if the amount of text to be printed is less than the size of the buffer. Otherwise, the computer will still have to wait for the buffer to partially empty before sending more text to the printer.

It is curious to note that, in fact, these built-in buffers are only a few thousand characters long—perhaps 2000 or 4000 characters. This is only a few pages of text, an amount you could almost wait for. It's for the long text that we humans would really like a buffer.

It seems that the *real* reason that such buffers came into vogue was to cure flow-control problems. If a printer can buffer only a linefull of text, then it is necessary for the printer to tell the computer to stop sending on a frequent basis. However, if the buffer is large, it takes quite a while for the buffer to fill, and there are opportunities for the printer to catch up somewhat.

Suppose we are talking about a 1200-baud (120 characters per second) communication to a printer which is rated at 150 characters per second. While printing lines of text, the printer keeps the queue of waiting characters quite short. However, if the printout contains a high number of linefeeds or pagefeeds, these are done much slower than 150 or even 120 per second. At the same time, characters are pouring into the buffer, starting to fill it up. Luckily, in a normal mix of text, you will soon return to high-speed, long lines of straight letters and numbers, and the printer can empty the buffer again. With this particular printer setup and a 2000- or 4000-character buffer, the text may never completely fill the buffer. You may never need to use a flow-control line.

But… suppose one day you decide to use the printer for long program listings containing lots of short lines, linefeeds and pagefeeds. Or perhaps you send it dot-addressable graphics. At this point, you may join the large group of printer users who discover, to their dismay, that there are chunks of program or picture missing from their printout. What has happened is that the printer's buffer filled up, and the printer had no way to stop the flow because no flow-control wire was ever installed!

The typical solution to this problem is to run the RS-232 interface slower, perhaps at 600 baud. But, if the printer is capable of sprinting along at 150 cps, why are we obliged to feed it only 60 cps?

Needless to say, buffers are **not** a cure for flow-control problems. They just get you out of the computer store happy and delay the problem until later. The right way to solve the problem is to set up proper flow control. If you want to test a setup which is *supposed* to have proper flow control (without monitoring gadgets), it is quite easy. All you have to do is get the computer to start sending a long printout to the printer. Then, deliberately disable the printer (press the Deselect or Offline button, or trigger the out-of-paper sensor). This should hang up the computer, either immediately, or after the printer's buffer is full. Work out how long it would take to fill the buffer at the baud rate chosen, then wait a little longer. Reactivate the printer, and see if the resulting printout has missed any of the information. Hanging up the computer is a definite indication of proper flow control. However, if the computer does not hang up, this *may* merely indicate that the computer is able to keep doing its own thing while the printer is busy, in which case, you must check the printout to determine whether flow control did its job.

Modems

Modems have a peculiarity which does not usually cause a problem, but has been known to bite people occasionally. The problem is known as *modem jitter*. A modem works by converting RS-232X data 1s and 0s into distinct tones, for transmission over the telephone lines. This is called *modulation*. At the other end, another modem listens to the tones, and decodes (or *demodulates*) them back into 1s and 0s. This is intended to be a recreation of what is happening at the transmission end. However, the whole process is less than precise, with the result that the exact transitions between 1s and 0s "jitter," they are not on the precise 3.33 milliseconds in a 300 baud example.

You may recall that it is these very transitions which the receiving equipment uses to stay in synchronization with the transmitter. The modem jitter will cause the receiver to attempt to correct when, in fact, it may not have been off to begin with!

Most RS-232X interfaces are managed by a UART (Universal Asynchronous Receiver-Transmitter) chip or other form of SIO (Serial Input/Output). These special-purpose chips are smart enough to correct their corrections and not get thrown off balance, and thus no problem is encountered with the jitter.

Some serial interfaces have been designed based upon a software UART. That is to say, the serial data wire just feeds into some input port of the system, and a program takes care of converting the stream of 1s and 0s into bytes, and also manages to stay in sync. (I assume here that you realize that almost every sort of peripheral equipment actually contains a microprocessor, and hence behaves as a preprogrammed, special-purpose "computer".) Unfortunately, such schemes sometimes don't work as well as their dedicated-chip counterparts when it comes to handling jitter. The resulting symptom is that of almost-correct operation, with intermittent (perhaps only once-a-week) garbage appearance.

You need not be too concerned about this problem in devices that are ordinarily connected to modems, such as terminals. It is more likely to occur in devices not normally used with modem-connection, such as dot-matrix printers. A well-known printer was saddled with this problem in its optional, serial-interface card. At least six different models of interface card appeared thereafter (some of which work), with confusion abounding among users desiring to use this printer in the listening-in mode. I should mention that since RS-232 is, after all, a standard for connection of a *terminal* to a *modem*, these users had every right to expect their printers to work from a modem when equipped with an "RS-232 Interface Card."

How Far Can You Run an RS-232X Line?

This is a question of much debate, but little has been done in the way of useful experimentation. Most books will tell you that 50 feet is the limit. By contrast, we have run six-conductor shielded cable up to 300 feet at 9600 baud with no problems. However, the longer the distance, the more capacitance there is in the cable which causes *rounding* of the data pulses as they appear on a scope.

Consequently, as length increases, data errors start to occur. However, you may still obtain satisfactory operation at slower baud rates. Don't be afraid to try it. In theory, you should be able to double the length if you halve the baud rate. Also, as you get near the limit, various different cables may work better or worse.

One strange anomaly should be mentioned in association with longer lines. Suppose you have a terminal connected to a computer that is 200 feet away. In normal, full-duplex operation, the remote computer echoes back what you type, and that is how characters appear on your screen. You would expect to have no operation from your terminal if the cable accidentally came disconnected at the computer end.

Well, surprise, surprise! The terminal may continue to display what you type! The reason is that, with a long cable, there can be enough capacitive coupling between your data-output wire and your (now disconnected and acting antenna-like) data-input wire, so that your output characters get into your terminal's input! (albeit, sometimes erroneously.) You will be convinced that the computer is still connected, but just acting stupid!

RS-232X Plastic-Box Interfaces

A fairly recent addition to the trials and tribulations of the RS-232X world is the *plastic box* interface. This is a plastic box about the size of a sandwich. Typically, it has a DB-25 on one end, and on the other end, a cable connecting the plastic box to the equipment to be adapted to RS-232X. One model I have seen connects to a printer's parallel Centronics input (an RS-232X-to-Centronics adapter). Another model appeared to be a general-purpose device, which, with some custom wiring by the manufacturer, would adapt a wide variety of equipment to RS-232X (such as calipers or small lab instruments).

When you see one of these gadgets, beware! Beware because the RS-232X signals they put out or accept may not be standard, so your test procedures must be applied with thought. The first point to investigate is the power source of the plastic box. Does it get 5 volts from Pin 18 of the Centronics connector? Does it have a 9-volt battery? Where does it get its plus and minus 12-volt supplies for putting out standard RS-232 signal levels?

While it is not technically impossible to generate plus and minus 12 volts from these lower voltages, I have found that they are often not generated, and the standard 1488 and 1489 RS-232 components are not used either. In fact, the units I have seen use CMOS components as driver and receiver, and may put out only 3- to 5-volt signals! There are barely enough to operate an RS-232 receiver at the other end of the cable, and insufficient to operate the unbuffered test gadgets presented in a previous chapter. One of the units even turned itself off to conserve power between bursts of data, leaving it's data output in a confusing (to us onlookers) floating state!

With the above cautions in mind, you can troubleshoot these plastic-box units. However, it remains to be seen whether they are really capable of functioning properly in diverse RS-232X situations.

Will New Chips Make Life Difficult?

As a continuation of the theme in the preceding paragraphs, it is worthwhile to warn that we may be seeing some new chips replacing the trusty 1488 and 1489 RS-232 driver and receiver. To an extent, a dangerous situation has developed in that much of the industry assumes that the 1488 and 1489 *are* RS-232. In fact, they work quite a bit better than the RS-232 minimum specifications.

For example, examining the test gadgetry, a typical RS-232 troubleshooting box will use LEDs powered off the RS-232 line using the voltage and current which it makes available. But, if a new series of chips replace the 1488 and 1489, we might see drivers which cannot light the LED indicators, nor drive the long cables which we now use, as already happens with the plastic box interfaces. Will it happen, or will this cause so much havoc that RS-232X will indeed be unofficially respecified to mean 1488 and 1489 or equivalent?

Hot tip for chip makers: There must be a market for a new chip containing one or two drivers *and* one or two receiver sections. If possible, throw in a small, power-inverter circuit to generate the plus and minus 12 volts. (You see, RS-232 is just about the last remaining thing in a computer which *still* needs a plus and minus 12-volt supply.)

A Case Study: Apple Meets Apple Printer

The following example illustrates how you must be prepared to fight your own disbelief, and demonstrates a few techniques in the bargain. It is the story of a group of highly-intelligent fellows connecting a new Apple IIe to a new Apple Imagewriter Printer, using a new Apple Super Serial Card, following the precise directions in the printer manual for *exactly* this set up.

It didn't work. Actually, the whole setup ran very well with the demonstration disk which was supplied with the printer. It gave us nice pictures of Einstein and maps in several sizes, which convinced us that the interfacing job was finished. However, if the system was freshly turned on and an attempt was made to use the printer using the PR #1 command (send all screen stuff to the printer), it flatly refused to budge.

Now what? Plow through the hundreds of pages of manuals on the Apple IIe, Super Serial and Imagewriter? Forget it. Call Apple dealer? Too late, store closed. Bring out the RS-232 monitor box!

The monitor revealed that data was definitely going to the printer, but the printer was ignoring it! Yet, the demo disk would work fine for graphics! Then it was discovered that the printer *would* work properly for text if the demo disk was run and a graphic image printed first! (By this time certain other text was getting pretty graphic, too.) Obviously, the demo software was changing some optional parameter of the RS-232 interface.

At a guess, we changed the Imagewriter's option switch so that it would look at only 7 bits instead of 8 bits. Presto! Now, it worked for text, but not for graphics! Then one of our team remembered (or was it a dream) that when Apples transmit 8-bit characters, the high-order bit is a 1 instead of a 0, which it should be, according to convention. Could the Imagewriter have been fazed by this naughty behavior? But both computer and printer were from the same company!

We didn't want to try to verify this hypothesis with a scope. Instead, we set about trying to fool the Super Serial Card into sending 8-bit characters with a high-order bit of 0. We needed to have the printer receive 8-bit characters so it could still handle the graphics. The Super Serial Card's parameters are changeable by sequences of codes, and we hoped to find the sequences which would make the necessary changes. Switch flipping then, would not be necessary for the two activities of text and graphics printing.

To accomplish this task, we drew on our knowledge of how different RS-232 data formats can look similar. For graphics, the format was 8 bits, and no parity. For text, we selected 7 bits, with parity, but with the parity bit permanently set to 0. This looks like 8-bits and no parity, with the highest order bit always 0! This was just the thing. Setting the Serial Card to this mode requires the key sequence Ctrl-I 7 P Ctrl-I 1 D, which can be incorporated into a short mode-setting program for convenience. A second program switches the interface back to it's initial mode for graphics work.

Manufacturers can't really expect you to figure all that out for yourself, can they? And if you think that's bad....you're sure to have some stories of your own before long!

Port Buddy Software: The RS-232 Helper

For serious, RS-232 troubleshooters with use of an IBM PC or clone, there is a software package which will be of interest. "Port Buddy" was written by my associate, Bill Morris, because it was badly needed. It makes light work out of a number of RS-232 jobs, from checking out baud rates and handshaking lines, to software development, or diagnosing problems in someone-else's commercial software.

Port Buddy is a utility which resides quietly in memory until you call it up. You can call it up at almost any time, including from within most applications programs. Port Buddy's windows overlay your current screen display, and immediately show you a variety of diagnostics for both COM1 and COM2 ports. Information includes present baud rate, data bits, stop bits and parity settings. Also shown on the screen are the states of all handshaking lines, and indicators for incoming data.

These features show how your computer's ports were set up by the software which last modified them. If you don't like those settings, or need to test different ones, Port Buddy allows you to change them.

One of Port Buddy's windows provides a terminal, so you can output data on the spot by keying it from the keyboard. Incoming data is displayed on the screen.

Finally, Port Buddy displays the state of the error bits in the serial chips, which lets you know what kind of problems might be hanging up communications.

As you can see, Port Buddy can be useful in many applications, the following are just a few examples.

Example 1: Setting Up a Serial Daisy-Wheel Printer

Let's suppose you've just received a bargain daisy-wheel printer by mail order. You later find out that this model was discontinued due to unusual function codes and a poorly written manual, which led to unpopularity. These features don't bother you, but you *do* have to get the machine set up by flipping some DIP switches and building the correct cable.

The manual is ambiguous on both the connector wiring and the DIP switches. You will have to try many options before you narrow in on the exact meaning of each connector pin and DIP switch.

In this case, you could use Port Buddy in combination with a test cable. Port Buddy will reveal what the printer is doing with its handshake wires, and, in addition, will allow you to control handshake wires fed to the printer.

At the same time, you can be quickly trying communication at a number of different baud rates and with various combinations of parity and stop bits via Port Buddy's terminal feature. The printer's responses, if any, will be displayed in Port Buddy's terminal window.

If you need to send a steady string of characters, you can use Port Buddy's autosend feature to send the same character repeatedly.

Example 2: Troubleshooting Commercial Software

Later that same day, you have successfully completed the cabling and switch setting and have obtained a simple printout of a file or a directory. Now, its time to install the printer under your new word processor.

The word processor just came in last week, and it's WonderWord, Rev 1.0. Miracle of miracles, it *does* have your printer on the menu, and everything seems to work smoothly. So, that evening, you attempt to print out that all-important research paper with the superscripts and subscripts. **Problem**! The superscripts and subscripts are reversed!

Well, right in the middle of printing, call up Port Buddy. You will not be able to see what the software is sending for superscript and subscript, but you can send those codes (as shown in the printer's manual) to test that the manual is correct. It would not be unusual for the manual to be mistaken, and for WonderWord's programmers to incorporate that error into the software.

Perhaps you will be able to correct WonderWord's problem by doing some sort of custom installation. Otherwise, you will just have to use your "evidence" to give you some credibility in contacting the WonderWord's creators.

Example 3: Software Development

If you wish to write software which must operate the PC's serial ports directly, you will appreciate Port Buddy's displays which show how the ports are set up. This feature will report to you whether your series of commands did what you expected, and will report on such important details as whether serial-port interrupts are enabled, and for what conditions.

Summary

Port Buddy is an invaluable tool, both for troubleshooting PC's and the operation of PC software, and for installing and diagnosing other RS-232 devices. For availability and price, contact VariousWare, P.O Box 21070, El Cajon, California, 92021.

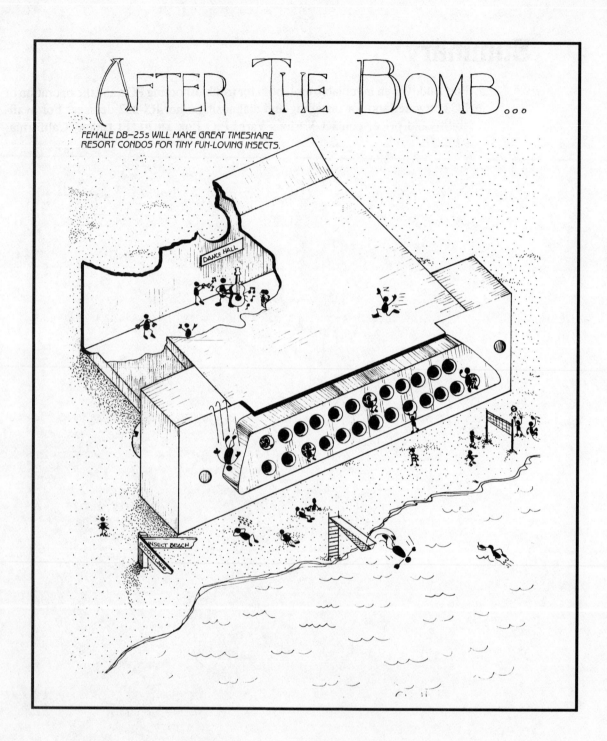

11

RS-232 Hardware: Cable and Connectors

I provide this chapter to tune you into the *good* hardware that's available, and, hopefully, to steer you away from the *really bad stuff*.

Ribbon Versus Individual-Wire Cable

There are basically two kinds of cable you can use: ribbon cable or the more familiar, multiconductor-in-a-jacket type of cable. Each kind has its own connectors.

Ribbon cable comes in various numbers of conductors, and we need 25 conductors for our purposes. The cable is flat, with the conductors laying side by side in the plastic ribbon. The conductors are usually .05 inches apart (1/20th of an inch), and are 26- or 28-gauge stranded wire. Be sure to choose these characteristics.

The DB-25 connectors used with ribbon cable are referred to officially as *Insulation Displacement Connectors* or *IDCs*, but they are often called *squash-ons*. Both names refer to the manner in which you assemble the connectors onto the cable. You merely insert the ribbon into the connector, lining up the ridges on the ribbon with the sharp spikes of the contacts, and then squash the assembly together in a vise. All 25 connections are made at once. Each contact pierces the insulation, and the conductor is wedged into the contact's sharp cleft. Little skill is involved, and the process is quick and easy.

Obviously, ribbon cable is most suited to straight-through cables, although, in a pinch, it can be used with a squash-on at one end and an individual-contact type of DB-25 plug at the other.

Mistakes You Can Make: There is some ribbon cable floating around that looks like what you want, but has the conductors on a slightly wider spacing, just enough that it doesn't quite work with common IDC DB-25. There are also some rare IDC DB-25 connectors floating around whose cable-gripping contacts are spaced slightly larger than .05 inch. These won't work with ordinary .05 inch ribbon cable. The confusion arises because DB-25 connector pins are slightly more than .05 inches apart. Older IDC DB-25s were constructed with wire-grippers on this wider spacing, thus requiring the wider-spaced ribbon cable. Present day IDC DB-25s have a more sophisticated internal structure, allowing them to work with ordinary .05 inch-spacing ribbon cable. So simply beware of "surplus" supply sources.

More Ribbon Cable Hints: All ribbon cable comes with some sort of colored stripes on it, some is even rainbow-colored, with each conductor being a separate hue. The plain cable will have one stripe, or perhaps one stripe every five or ten conductors. You should decide that a certain stripe will indicate Conductor 1 for you. When installing the connectors, inspect them for an indication of pin numbers molded into the plastic. At worst, there should be some sort of arrow, bump or dot next to Pin 1. Orient the cable so that the striped conductor comes out next to Pin 1.

On rainbow cable, the colors are of the same progression as the resistor color-code sequence, in which 1 is indicated by brown. The entire sequence is given in Table 11-1. Rainbow cable can be particularly useful if you must separate the conductors and solder them individually.

Note that there are four possible orientations for an IDC connector when assembling it onto the ribbon. Two orientations make identical connections, the other two are opposite to this. Play with the connector and cable in your hands to convince yourself of this. The two correct orientations are of course the ones where Pin 1 of the plug is next to Wire 1 of the cable. You can choose which of the two correct orientations is most convenient for the equipment to which you will be connecting. Usually, it is most convenient to have the cable drape downwards from the connector when it is plugged in.

Individual-Contact Hardware: A wide variety of solder-type, DB-25 hardware is available. In the most common type, 25 pins are already set into a connector block. Any sort of suitable-sized wire may be used with this arrangement. After soldering, a plastic shell is fastened around the assembly. The shell will protect the connections and provide some relief from strain.

Possibly the worst connector assemblies have been made this way. First of all, when you apply solder to the pins, the surrounding plastic melts and the pin moves out of location. Next, you find that, when connecting two adjacent pins, you have little means to prevent shorts between the two adjacent wires. (You should have used heat-shrink tubing for insulation, but who's got time to fiddle with that?) If you are *really* unlucky, you have obtained the hard black-plastic shells which have insufficient internal space, causing your wiring to be crushed together. These shells provide little in the way of strain relief, and the *ears* break off the first time the cable is dropped on the floor, taking chunks of the shell with them. This is the kind of connector you see a few months after installation—hooked to some poor

Table 11-1   Color-Coded Wire and Corresponding Pin Numbers

DB-25 Pin	Wire Number	Color Code
1	1	Brown
14	2	Red
2	3	Orange
15	4	Yellow
3	5	Green
16	6	Blue
4	7	Violet
17	8	Grey
5	9	White
18	10	Black
6	11	Brown
19	12	Red
7	13	Orange
20	14	Yellow
8	15	Green
21	16	Blue
9	17	Violet
22	18	Grey
10	19	White
23	20	Black
11	21	Brown
24	22	Red
12	23	Orange
25	24	Yellow
13	25	Green

secretary's word-processor terminal, wrapped in various varieties of tape, with a plaintive note attached, warning, "Please Don't Bump." This scenario has been illustrated in Figure 11-1.

Then there is *good* hardware. There is more than just one brand, but I am going to recommend AMP's products because they are darn good. This hardware has male and female connector blocks which initially contain no pins. The male and female pins come separately, and are individually soldered to the wires. The soldering process can be simplified by inserting the pins into a block of wood, which has been predrilled in two sizes to accomodate male and female pins snugly while they are being soldered. After soldering, the pins are pushed into the appropriate holes in the connector blocks from the rear. The holes in the blocks are deep, and designed so that, when the pin-and-wire combination is pushed in, the

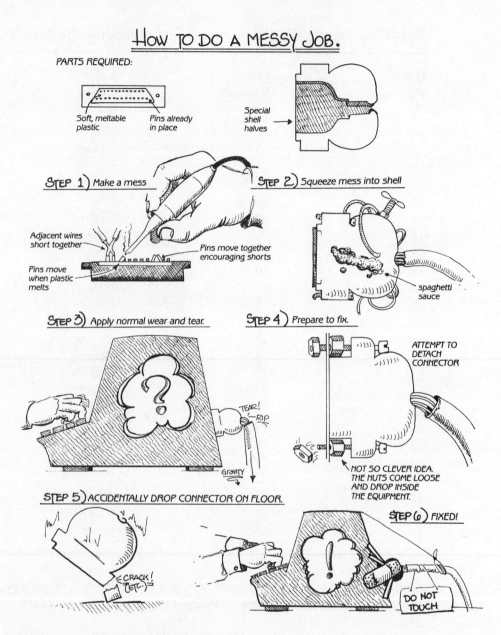

Figure 11-1   This is an illustration of the many ways *not* to connect a DB-25.

the wire is recessed into the hole, which separates it from the neighboring contacts and wires. In other words, there are no more shorts! The construction of the AMP DB-25 is shown in Figure 11-2.

The shells for these connectors are also a treat. They are made out of some sort of soft, resilient plastic, which is indestructible in normal use. The shell is designed so that the cable can be relieved of strain by attaching it to one of the shell-halves with an inexpensive, nylon wire tie. This has the added benefit that, if the

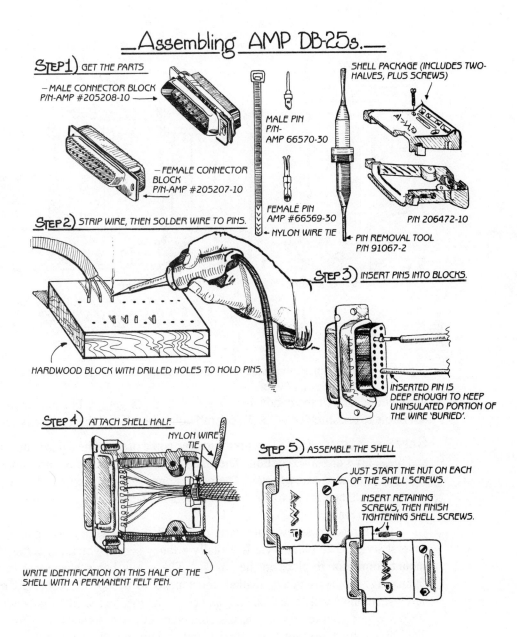

Assembling AMP DB-25s.

STEP 1) GET THE PARTS

— MALE CONNECTOR BLOCK
P/N-AMP #205208-10 ⟶

— FEMALE CONNECTOR
BLOCK
P/N-AMP #205207-10

MALE PIN
P/N-
AMP 66570-30

FEMALE PIN
AMP #66569-30

NYLON WIRE TIE

SHELL PACKAGE (INCLUDES TWO-
HALVES, PLUS SCREWS)

P/N 206472-10

PIN REMOVAL TOOL
P/N 91067-2

STEP 2) STRIP WIRE, THEN SOLDER WIRE TO PINS.

HARDWOOD BLOCK WITH DRILLED HOLES TO HOLD PINS.

STEP 3) INSERT PINS INTO BLOCKS.

INSERTED PIN IS
DEEP ENOUGH TO KEEP
UNINSULATED PORTION OF
THE WIRE 'BURIED'.

STEP 4) ATTACH SHELL HALF.

NYLON WIRE
TIE

WRITE IDENTIFICATION ON THIS HALF OF THE
SHELL WITH A PERMANENT FELT PEN.

STEP 5) ASSEMBLE THE SHELL

JUST START THE NUT ON EACH
OF THE SHELL SCREWS.

INSERT RETAINING
SCREWS, THEN FINISH
TIGHTENING SHELL SCREWS.

Figure 11-2 This illustrates the assembly of an AMP DB-25.

connector is later disassembled, half of the shell stays with the connector, so that any labeling done to that shell-half stays with the connector. The shells are grey, and can be labelled in permanent, felt-tip pen.

The same connector blocks (without their shells) can be used in chassis-mount situations.

Cable: As previously mentioned, if you are not using ribbon cable, then almost any old wire (of practical gauge) will do. It is convenient to use multiconductor

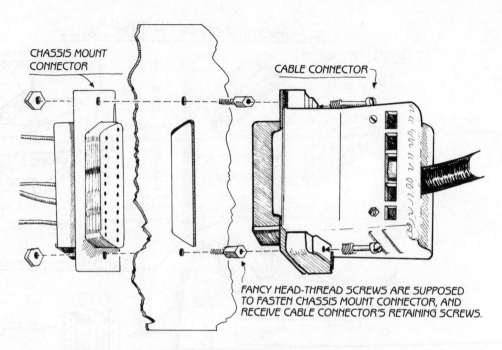

CHASSIS MOUNT CONNECTOR

CABLE CONNECTOR

FANCY HEAD-THREAD SCREWS ARE SUPPOSED TO FASTEN CHASSIS MOUNT CONNECTOR, AND RECEIVE CABLE CONNECTOR'S RETAINING SCREWS.

Figure 11-3   Diagram showing the fancy-head screws whose nuts always fall off.

wire where each of the conductors is about 22 or 24 gauge. For longer runs, it is advisable to use shielded wire. An overall outer shield is all that is usually required.

Screws, Etc.:   RS-232 seems to involve some of the silliest hardware around, and the screws are no exception. The chassis-mounted connectors are supposed to have two threaded screw holes. The cable connectors are supposed to have two screws which then fasten to the chassis-mount connector's holes, holding the cable connector in place.

The threaded, screw-hole parts of chassis-mount connector can be one of several styles. The older style is actually a fancy screw which holds the chassis-mount connector in place in the chassis. The screw has a hexagonal head (for tightening) which is nicely drilled and tapped to accept the cable connector's screws. In other words, the cable connector's screws thread into the heads of the screws which are holding the chassis connector in place, as shown in Figure 11-3. This looks good, except that, after a few cablings and uncablings, the cable-connector's screws invariably get stuck in the chassis-connector's screw head. This will eventually loosen it to the point where the nut inside the cabinet which holds the connector to the chassis will fall off, causing the whole chassis connector to eventually drop off. By the time you get around to fixing it, you've lost the fancy, hex-head, tapped-out screw, and you end up using a regular screw anyway.

A newer style is seen where the chassis's DB-25 is actually mounted on an internal circuit board, and hence does not need to use the two fancy screws for support. The two screw holes in the connector ears are already threaded to accept the screws of the cable connector. Too bad somebody forgot that, in this arrangement, the cable-connector's screws are not going to be long enough to reach the specially threaded holes. This keeps you from discovering that some of the circuit-board-mounted connectors with the nicely threaded hole use a different thread anyway; so even if the screws *were* long enough, you couldn't get them in.

Inquiries for AMP Products

For the name of a distributor of AMP products in your area, write to:

AMP Industries,
Box 3608
Harrisburg, PA 17105
Phone: 717-564-0100

12

Centronics Parallel Interface

In contrast to the frustration caused by the extreme lack of standardization in RS-232X interfaces, the Centronics parallel interface is, generally, very simple to work with. The interface is named for the Centronics Company, whose printers first popularized the system. It is almost always used with a particular kind of connector, and the signals are always in the same place. Except for a few oddballs and mainframe-type printers, whenever a printer is described as *parallel*, this is the kind of interface you should expect it to have.

The Normal Centronics Interface Arrangement

Figure 12-1 shows a picture of the female Centronics connector as you see it on a printer. Both printers and computers will usually have a female Centronics connector, so the cable needed will have a male Centronics plug on both ends. Such a cable is most readily and reliably constructed using 36-conductor ribbon cable, (although you usually only need 25-conductor cable or less) and IDC squash-on Centronics connectors.

The Signals

The Centronics signals and their functions are listed in Table 12-1. The system uses eight wires which carry character data from the computer to the printer; with data flowing only in one direction. An additional wire, (*STB Data Strobe), sends pulses from the computer to tell the printer that the data is ready. The printer uses two wires to indicate to the computer that it may proceed. These wires are: *BUSY*,

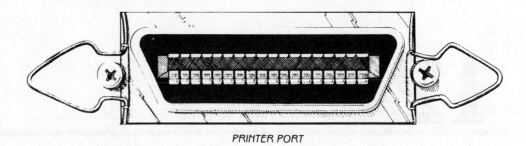

PRINTER PORT

Figure 12-1   This is the female Centronics connector as seen on the printer, and on some computers.

whose state indicates whether the printer is currently able to accept more data; and *ACK* which pulses at the end of BUSY. (These two signals are a little redundant, and, in fact, some computers only look at one of them. However, you should hook up *both* to be certain.)

The printer also has several other output wires to send messages back to the computer, indicating a variety of not-ready conditions; however, rarely are these all used by the computer and its software.

Finally, there is an input wire to the printer which the computer uses to *initialize* the printer. This will return the printer to default or starting values. This is not usually necessary, since codes can be sent on the data line to perform this function.

A Popular Variation on the Cabling

Sometimes a computer will provide a parallel printer-output port, but it will not use a Centronics connector. Sometimes a DB-25 will be used. In many such situations, the signals are arranged on the DB-25 so that the needed cable can use a Centronics IDC at the printer end, and an IDC DB-25 at the computer end. This cable can be 25-conductor ribbon. The Centronics connector is installed so that Pins 1-13 and 19-30 are the only ones contacting the conductors, and the remainder are not used. This can be shown in Figure 12-2.

Beware, the occasional equipment which uses a DB-25 and whose pin functions are not in this convenient order, or whose connector may have other, non-Centronics signals on it. This is the case with some IDS (Integral Data Systems) printers. **Check the manual first!**

Also, it is very necessary to make sure that an RS-232 cable is **never** plugged into a Centronics DB-25, because the RS-232 signals will damage those chips in the computer which are wired to the Centronics connector!

Table 12-1   Centronics Signals

Pin	Abbrev	Name/Function	From
1	*STB	Data Strobe: Printer should latch in data on the low-to-high transition.	Computer
2	D1	Data bit 1 (lowest order bit)	Computer
3	D2		
4	D3		
5	D4		
6	D5		
7	D6		
8	D7		
9	D8	Data bit 8 (highest order bit)	Computer
10	*ACK	Low means printer has finished processing character, ready for next	Printer
11	BUSY	High means don't send more data	Printer
12	Paper Out	High means paper run out	Printer
13	SEL	"Select", high indicates printer is active and "on line".	Printer
14	SG	Signal ground	
16	SG	Signal ground	
17	CG	Chassis ground	
18	+5 volt	+5 volt supply (do NOT wire through!)	
19 to 30		"Twisted pair return". Generally regarded as just another signal ground but useable for the ground wire of twisted-pair cable.	
31	*IP	Input Prime: Low means initialize printer. Usually this can also be done by sending the printer a special code as data.	Computer
32	*FAULT	Low indicates some problem has occurred.	Printer
33	SG	Signal ground	
15, 34, 35 and 36 are unused			

Note: * means active low.

1. Signals are TTL levels, so 2.4V to 5V means high, and 0 to 0.8V means low.

2. Data lines are sometimes referred to as D0 to D7.

3. Data lines are non-inverted, low = 0, high = 1.

4. On some equipment the high-order data line may not be used. If a computer does not provide this line, but the printer needs it, you cannot generally just leave it unconnected. TTL inputs which are left unconnected are pulled high so appear as a logic one. This would cause the printer to think it is receiving characters whose highest bit is a one, which results in graphics characters on many printers. Instead, wire this line to ground (logic zero).

Another Popular Variation: The IBM PC

The IBM PC and many PC-compatibles use a DB-25 connector for the Centronics printer output. To make a cable for this setup, assemble a 25-conductor ribbon cable with a DB-25 connector at one end and a Centronics connector at the other, as just described. This arrangement will not work *yet*, however, since the bottom row of pins at the DB-25 (Pins 14-25) are connected to ground at the printer end.

Unfortunately, the PC uses some of those bottom pins for special uses. Pin 15, for example, indicates a printer error when the signal is low. Luckily, all we have to do is to chop through the ribbon conductor which connects to DB-25 Pin 15; the

Looking at the contacts of a male...

1	2	3	4	5	6	7	8	9	10	11	12	13	14	15	16	17	18
o	o	o	o	o	o	o	o	o	o	o	o	o	o	o	o	o	o
o	o	o	o	o	o	o	o	o	o	o	o	o	o	o	o	o	o
19	20	21	22	23	24	25	26	27	28	29	30	31	32	33	34	35	36

How these connect to DB-25 pins in a ribbon cable situation:

TopRow Centronics:

1   2   3   4   5   6   7   8   9   10   11   12   13   14 to 18 DB-25:
1   2   3   4   5   6   7   8   9   10   11   12   13 Not connected

Bottom Row

Centronics: 19   20   21   22   23   24   25   26   27   28   29   30 31 to 36
DB-25:   14   15   16   17   18   19   20   21   22   23   24   25 Not connected

Figure 12-2   Numbering of Centronics connector contacts, and how these connect to DB-25 when using a ribbon cable.

PC's internal input pull-up resistors will cause our disconnected error-indicator to rise to a no-error signal level. You might, instead, chop out Pin 15 on the DB-25, so as to avoid signalling an error condition to the PC. This is illustrated in Figure 12-3.

With this cable, the operation of some printers is not quite so elegant as with a real cable. With the proper wiring as listed in Table 12-2, it is possible for the software to find out more about certain error conditions in the printer. In addition, the PC's boot-up routine will reset the printer. However, I have yet to see software which cares about fancy error conditions, nor a printer which really benefits from this booting-up resetting. (You can reset the printer yourself whenever you choose anyway.)

A PC Printer Problem (Parallel and Serial Models)

There is a problem which you may encounter with some PC or PC-compatible computers. While the printer is printing, you get a message on the screen saying that there is an error on the PRN device. Before getting too excited, simply "retry" by keying the letter R.

Let me describe what happens. In some versions of the operating system, the printer output routine will not wait long enough for the printer to become ready, and assumes that there is a problem. This is particularly noticeable with (slow) daisy-wheel printers equipped with a long character buffer. Although characters can be sent into the buffer smoothly, when the buffer fills up it may be some time before the printer will signal that it is ready to accept more characters. It is during this period that the operating system thinks that the printer has "died."

Fortunately, this problem is easy to fix, and if you have just read your MSDOS/PCDOS manual from end to end, you would already know the solution. All you have to do is to tell the operating system to wait longer! This is done on real PCs and some compatibles using the MODE utility, and on other compatibles using some other utility (Zenith calls their utility CONFIGUR). It's probably the same utility that sets the baud rate and so on, and you should look up precisely how to do it, because different machines are different in this respect.

Other Centronics Variations

Naturally, you couldn't expect any standard to be *truly standard*, so there are some variations to keep you amused. Radio Shack, for example, uses a PC-board edge-connector as a Centronics connector on some of their computers. There are others I am told, but you should be able to spot them when you see them.

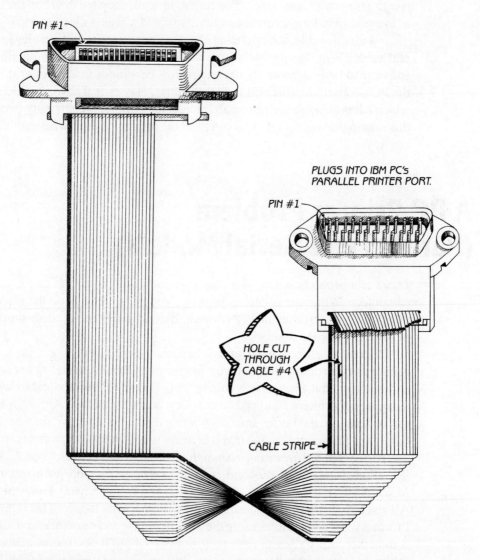

PLUGS INTO PARALLEL (CENTRONICS) PRINTER.

PIN #1

PLUGS INTO IBM PC's
PARALLEL PRINTER PORT.

PIN #1

HOLE CUT
THROUGH
CABLE #4

CABLE STRIPE →

Figure 12-3 This illustration shows how to make a quick and dirty PC printer cable in about 2 minutes.

Problems with "Real" Centronics Cables

There are actually two problems. First of all, some manufacturers bring out a +5-volt supply voltage on Pin 18. This is intended to run some external gadget board, for example, a serial-to-parallel converter box. By my not-too-large statistical

Table 12-2

PC DB25	Printer Centronics		PC DB25	Printer Centronics	
1	1	*Strobe	14	14	*AutoFeed
2	2	Data 1	15	32	*Error
3	3	Data 2	16	31	*Init
4	4	Data 3	17	36	*Select
5	5	Data 4	18	NC	
6	6	Data 5	19	19	Gnd
7	7	Data 6	20-24	NC	
8	8	Data 7	25	30	Gnd
9	9	Data 8			
10	10	*Ack	All non-data outputs from PC		
11	11	Busy	are open-collector types and may be		
12	12	Paper End	shorted to ground without		
13	13	Select	damage.		

analysis, it seems that printers should have this feature, and computers should not. However, if you get a computer and a printer which both do this, and then use a 36-conductor, all-wires-connected cable, the two +5-volt lines will be connected together. This situation will not be tolerated by at least one of the power supplies involved. It can result in just a blown fuse, or perhaps even worse damage.

To get around this problem, store-bought Centronics cables are often assembled with only 34-conductor ribbon cable. This is a suitable remedy. However, consider the possibility that the poor laborer who assembles these cables now has an extra opportunity to make a mistake. Not only can one of the connectors be installed wrong-way-around, but it might have the ribbon offset by one or two conductors, since it is no longer guided into position by its snug-fitting width. Moral: Always check your store-bought cables before use.

A Closer Look at Centronics Signals

In some cases, it is necessary to get a bit more involved in the actual signals on the Centronics cable. In particular, the Centronics specification is a little redundant in that there are two signals by which the printer can signal that it is ready for more input. On some computers only one is used, and the supplied cable only connects that one signal. This can cause confusion if that cable is passed on to a different application.

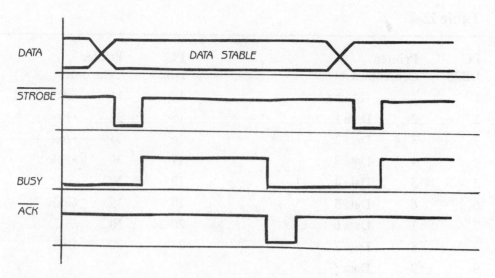

Figure 12-4   Diagram showing timing of the Centronics signals involved in the passing of data.

In other cases, it may be necessary to make a cable for an oddball printer with a non-standard connector and innovative nomenclature. Finally, you may wish to build an interface project that can hook onto a Centronics port, and can be accessible through regular printer commands. Chapter 21 presents some simple Centronics interface ideas which do not require faking these signals, but which require direct software access to the Centronics port. In any case, a closer look at the signals is in order.

Referring to Figure 12-4, we can follow the sequence of events. First of all, the computer places some data on the data output wires. After fractions of a microsecond, the cable carries valid data. Next, the computer signals to the printer that data is ready by pulsing the STROBE* line for a few microseconds. Within fractions of a microsecond, the printer responds by raising the BUSY line to high.

After some time (microseconds to seconds, depending on the fullness of the printer's buffer memory), the printer has finished and changes the BUSY line to low. At the same time, the printer pulses the ACKNOWLEDGE* line for a few microseconds.

So, we have two signals which indicate that the printer is ready to go. Conceivably, the original plan may have been to use the busy line with computer systems which sit in a loop waiting for the BUSY to be finished, the ACK* pulse was for use with machines which could do something else while waiting, and be interrupted when another character was needed.

We now have support chips in computers which can interrupt the main processor on a signal transition, and thus, the BUSY line could be used for interruption, so one BUSY line would be adequate. On the other hand, an ACK* line by itself would *not* be adequate, since it cannot be used at an arbitrary time to see if the printer is ready for data—at the beginning of a printout, for example.

13

How Video Systems Work

In order to discuss all of the different video connection conventions that exist, it is first necessary to discuss how a picture is drawn on a computer's screen. In fact, we will discuss how a television screen works, since the computer's screen is really a descendant of television.

Of CRTs and Electron Beams

What commercials and television repairmen refer to as a "picture tube" on your television set is called a *cathode ray tube* or CRT. Just in case you've never looked inside your television or computer monitor, I've included a sketch of what it looks like in Figure 13-1. There are three tricky things about a CRT.

1. A coating of a material called *phosphor* has been painted on the inside of the viewing surface of the CRT. Phosphor glows when struck by electrons.

2. An apparatus called an *electron gun* is incorporated into the neck of the CRT. The gun launches a thin beam of electrons toward the phosphor-coated face. The apparatus includes a means by which to control the intensity of the beam, and hence the brightness of the spot on the screen.

3. A set of coils are mounted around the neck of the tube. These coils, under control of some circuitry, are able to deflect the beam so that it can strike anywhere on the surface of the CRT.

You can readily see that with this apparatus, it is possible to draw pictures on the screen. You might imagine that the beam would probably move around much as we move a pencil on paper, but, this is not the way television operates.

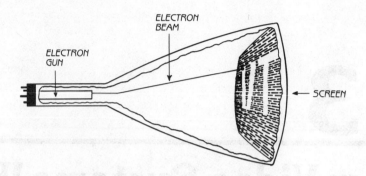

Figure 13-1 The no-doubt familiar picture of the insides of a picture tube, more respectably known as a cathode ray tube or CRT.

Scanning

The electron beam always follows a scanning pattern. First, it moves to the top left corner. Then it sweeps horizontally over to the top right corner, dropping just slightly. Then it is quickly retraced back to the left side to a position just below its previous position. Then sweep back over to the right, dropping slightly. And so the beam proceeds until it has covered the entire screen.

As the beam is passing over the entire screen, its brightness is varied very quickly to form the details which become the picture. Finally, the beam is returned to the top of the screen, where the process starts over again.

This method of drawing a picture is called the *raster method*, and a single line is sometimes called a *raster line*, or simply a *raster*.

How Many Lines . . .

In North America, there are 262.5 raster lines made on the screen on each vertical passage. Not all of those are actually used for the picture. Some are used up in the areas that are off the top and bottom of the screen, and some are consumed during the retrace from bottom to top of screen. It takes about 64 microseconds per horizontal trace, which is about 15750 lines per second. This means that the whole screen is covered in about 1/60th of a second. Actually that's a slight untruth, because of something called *interlace*.

It turns out that engineers had quite a compromise to face when they first tackled television. First of all, they wanted as many raster lines as possible on the screen, so as to be able to show fine vertical details. On this basis 525 lines were picked as a satisfactory number. Another consideration was that the screen be redrawn at least 60 times per second. If the screen was *refreshed* much less often, the eye would see a distracting flicker. Finally, they had to pay attention to how fast they could vary the intensity of the electron beam. The faster the horizontal scan, the faster the electron beam would have to be fluctuated in order to show the same horizontal detail.

Actually, this problem concerning the speed of fluctuation was not a problem at the electron beam, per se. However, the faster the electron-beam brightness has to be fluctuated, the more space each television channel would take up in the broadcast spectrum. In other words, each channel would have a wider *bandwidth*. So, it was a case of more detail and less channels, or vice versa.

Luckily, a trick called "interlace" allows us to obtain a two-fold improvement. Instead of making the electron beam draw every line on each screen passage, we make the beam do every other line on the first pass, and the intervening lines on the next pass, which makes 262.5 lines per pass. This effectively deals with the flicker problem because it refreshes the overall brightness of the screen once per 1/60th of a second, while allowing us to use the combination of the "slow" 64 microseconds per horizontal scan with a nice vertical resolution of 525 total lines to provide detail.

Each of the passes over the screen is called a *field*, and the two fields which make up a completed picture are called a *frame*. Although we have a total of 525 lines, perhaps only 480 lines (240 per field) are useful for actually showing the picture. The remainder are consumed by the vertical retrace.

To facilitate some coming discussions, I mention here that computer-video systems often do not use interlace. Instead, they merely use 262 lines repeated 60 times a second. This is almost analogous to an interlaced system with the two fields of each frame being identical. However, the two fields are positioned identically, not shifted up and down a line.

Television Video

The black-and-white (B&W) television video signal provides three sets of information:

1. It has a component which tells the beam when to return to the top of the screen and start a new picture. This is called the *vertical sync*. After the vertical-sync pulse, the television set, itself, is responsible for gradually sweeping down the screen, until about 1/60th of a second later, when a new vertical-sync pulse is received.

2. There is a component in the signal which tells the beam when to return to the left side of the screen and start a new horizontal line. This is called *horizontal sync*. After the horizontal-sync pulse the television set is responsible for scanning the beam smoothly over to the right side. About 64 microseconds later, another horizontal-sync-pulse arrives to start a new scan line.

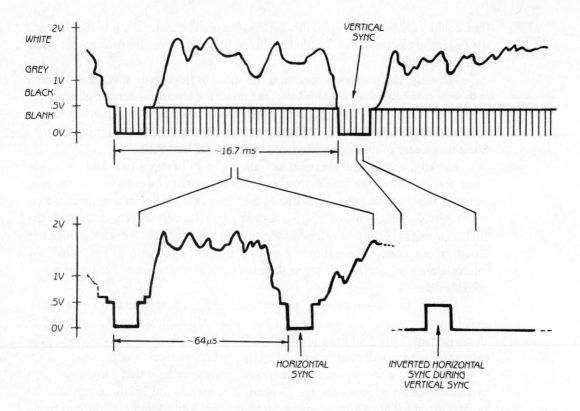

Figure 13-2   A typical composite video signal, shown on two time scales. Shown above is almost two fields of signal, while below is a single horizontal line.

3. The third component is, of course, the signal which actually controls the brightness of the beam as it scans along. It is this signal which is most responsible for actually making the picture appear. This signal is sometimes called *luminance*.

A typical, television-style, video signal is shown in Figure 13-2. This is the sort of signal you might see coming from a video camera for a VCR or what have you. This is called *composite monochrome video*, because one signal contains all three vital parts of the video information.

This is **not** what goes into a television set directly from an antenna or cable-television system. The antenna/cable signal is in a somewhat different form, suitable for transmission via radio waves. At the television station, a video signal was *modulated* onto the radio frequency signal of a specific channel, which carries it to your house. There it is received by your antenna and fed to your television set. The television's *tuner* selects which channel to use, then demodulates the signal to recover the video (and also the audio), which then is used to control the television's video section. Cable television works similarly, except that the distribution is over a cable instead of by radio waves.

Color

In a color system, a special color CRT is used. This has three different phosphors, (red, green and blue) painted carefully on the screen in a pattern of tiny dots or stripes. Illuminating these colors in various combinations can produce virtually any desired color on the television screen. There are three electron beams, and a perforated metal mask, arranged so that each beam can only hit one color of phosphor. Thus, we can consider that we have red, green and blue beams.

Now, we need signals to control the color. You might think we need three separate color signals, one for each beam. In fact, at some stage inside the television set, we do, indeed, need three separate control signals. However, for purposes of transmission and reception, this is not necessary.

It turns out that it is possible to choose an alternate signal convention for specifying what is to be shown at each "point" on the screen. From the original black-and-white system we already have a brightness signal. To that we can add two other signals, called *chroma* and *saturation*. Chroma picks the color (is it red, or blue, or orange etc.), while saturation describes how much color the point has (mostly white with a tinge of color, or mostly color . . .).

When color television was introduced, the chroma and luminance signals were thrown into the composite video signal in a somewhat technical manner which permitted compatibility with existing B&W sets. But, unfortunately, some compromise was entailed, as we shall see. It is not necessary to understand how the color signals were included in order to understand the compromises, but it is briefly described here for those who would like to know.

Color Complexity

Technically speaking, the color information is carried on a 3.58-megahertz (MHz) carrier signal. The chroma signal *phase modulates* the carrier, while the saturation *amplitude modulates* the carrier.

What this means is that there is a sine wave (of frequency 3.58 million cycles per second) added into the composite video. The amplitude is varied according to the color saturation seen by the camera at that point, while the phase is varied according to the actual color being selected. If the sine wave is at one phase, that represents one color. If it is shifted over (delayed or advanced slightly) it picks a different color, and so on.

The question quickly arises, "how does the receiver know which is which phase angle?" Obviously, some reference must be provided. This is done by including a reference burst of 3.58-megahertz sine wave at an inconspicuous location, namely, right after each horizontal sync pulse. This is enough to keep the television's internal, 3.58-megahertz reference oscillator synchronized to the television station's idea of *zero phase*. Then, during the beam's scan across the screen, the incoming, phase-modulated, 3.58-megahertz chroma signal is constantly compared to the internal reference to arrive at a difference angle which picks the color.

Color Problems

Composite color works reasonably well for ordinary television purposes, however, it is based on a trick. In fact, the actual rate at which the chroma and saturation signals can be varied is rather slow. This means that color details on the screen are blurry and imprecise. We can get away with this on ordinary television because the luminance signal *does* vary rapidly and makes the details sharp in brightness, if not in color.

It is as though the picture is sharply drawn in black and white, with watercolors sloppily painted over the top. If you have ever seen this artists' technique, you will realize that the eye is not very particular about how the colors fit the details—at least not for ordinary television viewing.

For computer use, however, we frequently demand much greater resolution and far sharper color details than such a system can provide. Notice that this is not really a fault of the CRT system, it is merely a fault of the signal system which television uses to convey information.

For this reason, composite color is one of the worst signal conventions for computer monitors, and is generally passed over in favor of other systems which use multiple wires to control the colors separately, as we shall see.

Resolution

Much is heard about the *resolution* or detail-drawing ability of a particular monitor or system, both in computers and in entertainment video, and again, the terminology is confusing.

There are several different ways to look at resolution. The first way is that of the photographer or microscopist, who discuss resolution in terms of lines per inch. This refers to the maximum density of lines which can be distinctly picked out by the camera or microscope. Literally, a piece of card with stripes printed on it may be placed in front of the camera, and a photo taken to test this measurement.

This same test may also be applied to a video camera or video signal generator used in conjunction with a VCR or monitor, to test the overall resolution of such a system. However, resolution is no longer described as "per inch," but, instead, as "per screen" to enable the comparison of monitors of different CRT sizes. In addition, in the video world we might expect to find a difference in resolution in the vertical and horizontal directions.

In fact, in the vertical direction, it is pretty obvious that the resolution is limited by the number of raster lines at best. But is the resolution equal to the number of displayed raster lines (about 480 if interlaced)? Not if we go by the photographers' ideas, because on one raster we may show a line, while on the next we show a space, on the next a line and so forth! This is the best we can do, so we must say that according to a photographer, the vertical resolution is at most only about 240 lines per screen, if interlaced, or 120 if not.

However, in the computer field, when speaking of graphics, resolution is usually specified in terms of how many *pixels* or dots can be displayed vertically or horizontally. The IBM PC's normal graphics card displays 200 horizontal lines of pixels with 640 pixels in each line. Thus the vertical resolution might be described as 200 lines (of pixels) or 100 lines, (photographer-wise). Naturally, the computer market adopts the higher number as its method of description.

In the horizontal direction, resolution is not limited by a factor such as the number of rasters. In a monochrome monitor, the phosphor is just a continuous painted coat, so the resolution is only limited by how fine a beam we can focus, and how quickly the beam can be turned on and off. In a color monitor, however, the phosphor is not continuous, but rather, there are vertical stripes, or threesomes of dots of the three colors of phosphors. The density of such stripes or threesomes is thus a limiting factor for resolution in color monitors.

Very good entertainment-video monitors might be rated at 300 to 350 lines of horizontal resolution "at the center." This means that if a picture was shown having 300 vertical lines, then you could pick them out at the middle of the CRT, but at the edges they would be fuzzy.

Let's compare this to computer situation monitors. In order to draw 300 vertical lines you would need 600 pixels horizontally, alternating on and off. Thus, a computer monitor whose horizontal resolution was stated as 600 pixels is about equivalent in resolution to an entertainment monitor rated at 300 lines.

Notice, however, that, in the case of the entertainment monitor (since we are dealing with composite video) this is a rating of luminance resolution, not chroma (color selection) resolution. This means that this type of monitor is not optimum for computer video, since high-resolution computer video requires a high color resolution. Also, in the discussion on bandwidth which follows, we will see that this much resolution is not even useful with ordinary TV signals, but only with high-quality video sources, such as video disks.

Bandwidth

This is another term which often comes up in discussing monitors and video machinery. In fact, so far as we are concerned, bandwidth is merely an alternate way to specify resolution. You will have noticed that an important variable in resolution is how fast the electron beam can be switched on and off. Indeed, if any part of the video chain limits that ability, it limits resolution. Bandwidth is a figure which gives the most rapid rate at which the beam can be fluctuated, and it is measured in megahertz (MHz).

For a screen containing 80 characters per line with 8-by-9 pixels per character, we need to draw a maximum of 640 dots horizontally. If adjacent pixels are on, it will not be necessary to extinguish the beam between them. However, if two pixels which are on are separated by a single pixel which is off, then it will be necessary for the beam to be clearly off between the two pixels which are on. Thus the maximum number of on-off cycles we must be able to handle is 320 on-off cycles per raster.

This must all happen in the time it takes for one raster. Although 64 microseconds are used per raster, the text will occupy an area representing a width of only about 45 microseconds. So, 320 cycles in 45 microseconds gives us a rate of about 7 million cycles per second, or 7 megahertz. This is the absolute minimum bandwidth necessary for a somewhat reasonable 80-column display, and, in fact, our calculation is rather approximate because it permits the beam to turn on and off quite slowly.

Higher bandwidth would permit the same display to appear sharper and clearer. Inexpensive monitors are available with bandwidths up to 15 megahertz. By contrast, the ordinary television set has a bandwidth limited to about 3.5 megahertz, which explains why it is only useful up to 40 column displays.

To relate this topic back to a previous discussion, this bandwidth figure is directly proportional to the amount of radio space allocated to each TV station. You are probably familiar with the FM radio band, stretching from 88 megahertz to 108 megahertz. TV stations are allocated nearby frequencies; for example, Channels 2 to 6 use the space from 54 to 88 megahertz (except for 72 to 76 megahertz) with 6 megahertz allocated to each. This accomodates 3.5 megahertz of picture (luminance), color, and sound.

14

Computer Video Signals

Working with video signals rarely causes major problems. Most problems are simply a matter of picking the right product for the job. So, working with video is mostly a question of understanding the terminology involved, the variations of equipment which are available, and the results that may be expected.

Differences Between Television and Computer Video Pictures

There are a number of serious differences between typical television-picture material and the images we see on computer screens. First of all, television pictures are drawn by continuous scan lines, while the computer makes pictures with dots or *pixels*. The beam-scanning process is the same, but to draw the dots, we have to be able to turn the beam on and off rapidly and sharply to present the fine details of small letters and numbers or other graphics.

Secondly, in a normal television picture, there is an interest in intermediate brightness levels (grey areas), while in computers, grey areas are used less. Some computers can produce no intermediate intensities at all, while others can produce only a few.

Finally, there are some points to be made about interlace. Many, if not most computers do not use interlace at all. (Not using interlace is sometimes called *random interlace*). These computers have a maximum of only about 230 lines of useful video information, (although 262 lines are produced in total), and each frame is actually two identical fields. To be completely honest, some computers don't even put out an accurate number of lines, perhaps only 256!

A typical screen containing 25 rows of 80 characters will use perhaps a 7-by-9 matrix of dots for each character. With 25 rows of 9, you would only require 225 lines. So you can see, interlace is not necessary for ordinary text.

Other computers, however, are capable of displaying graphics which can require perhaps 400 or even 480 lines of useful video (with a total of 525 lines in a frame). Obviously, if a standard monitor is to be used, the display *must* interlace. Notice, by the way, that interlace is *not* a property of the monitor, it is all in the computer's control of the video signal. Herein lies a problem.

Remember that the reason that we can "get away" with a frame repetition rate as low as 30 frames per second is because, in a normal television picture, the overall brightness of the screen is refreshed every field, or 60 times per second, avoiding the sensation of flicker. In computer graphics, however, we might find details so thin that they are present in only one of the fields. An example would be a horizontal line which was one pixel wide. This line will only be refreshed 30 times a second, and will indeed appear to flicker.

All of these differences between television and computer video are reflected in the way computer video monitors are designed. These differences also influence the signal conventions.

Variations in Computer Video Systems

There are quite a few video signal conventions in use today, and these vary in the following aspects:

1. Signals are either black and white signals or are color signals.

2. The intensity of the beam(s) can be varied (*analog* or *continuous tone*), or the beam(s) are either full-on or full-off (*digital*).

3. They also vary in the ways in which the sync signals are provided.

"Modulated" Television Output

Let us first dispose of the situations where a real television set is the computer's screen. A computer which requires a television will have an output which imitates the type of signal coming from a television station. This is only the case with a few of the very inexpensive computers, such as Radio Shack's Color Computer. The instructions will tell you how to hook the computer to the television set, and will say what channel to tune to on the television. You may have a choice of channel, as selected by a switch on the computer, in order to avoid interference from some local television station.

For computers with composite-video output, it is possible to buy a device called a *video modulator*. This device takes the composite video and makes an imitation television-type signal out of it so that you can feed that into a television set.

In my opinion, using a television set as a computer screen is not worthwhile. It produces blurry images, miserable colors, and is susceptible to electrical noise which appears on the screen as "snow" or unwanted patterns. It is disappointing with text of 40 columns or less, and is unusable with text denser than 40 columns. In fact, if you use a real television set, the image is degraded by the television's own circuitry which deliberately cuts down on detail—detail which is not normally present in an ordinary television signal, but which is put out by the computer.

I therefore recommend that television sets not be used for serious computer operation.

Composite Video — One Color (Monochrome)

This is the normal output provided by most computers, and expected by most one-color monitors. These monitors may be black and white, or the color may be green, yellow or some other single color. You can choose phosphors of different *persistences*, that is, the characteristic length of time an image takes to fade on the computer's screen. A long persistence screen is particularly useful for high-resolution, interlaced computer video, to reduce 30 hertz flicker.

The composite signal is as described in the preceding chapter, although this may be simplified in a number of ways. An example would be the omission of horizontal sync pulses during the vertical sync. There are some other variations:

1. This is NOT the "monochrome" as the term is applied to IBM-PC's so called *monochrome card*. I'll explain this later.

2. The computer may, or may not, be able to produce different intensities at each pixel on the screen. By this we mean various degrees of brightness or dimness, or shades of grey. If it can produce different intensities, you will want to check that the monitor can reproduce them.

3. Monitors can be obtained with either analog or digital intensity. Analog intensity means that the beam can be controlled to various brightnesses for different pixels. Digital means that the incoming signal is interpreted as either bright or dark and the beam is switched on or off accordingly. This can make for sharper text, but causes an inability to show different intensities.

    Note that even digital monitors have brightness and contrast controls to adjust the screen appearance. Also, digital monitors obviously cannot usefully display analog video signals, such as from cameras or video cassette recorders.

4. Analog monitors intended for use with cameras or video cassette recorders will work with computers to some extent, but are often equipped with internal circuitry which tends to limit details, and are not suitable for long-term viewing.

Non-Composite, Direct Drive One-Color Monitors

These are rarely encountered as separate items, but are frequently used in equipment with built-in or dedicated screens, such as the Kaypro, the Zenith Z-100 "All-In-One", various PC-clone portables, the Terak series, most terminals, and so on.

This signal system uses one wire for beam intensity (our luminance signal) and then has one or two additional wires for horizontal and vertical synchronization.

A common arrangement has two separate sync-like wires, called *Horizontal Drive* and *Vertical Drive*. These are generally TTL-level signals (0 volts = low, 3 to 5 volts = high), and, although they provide the synchronization function, they are usually quite a bit wider than sync pulses would be. The usual polarity seems to be normally low, pulsing high; however, don't be surprised to find the inverse.

There are other non-composite systems, but they are all pretty similar to non-composite color systems, which I discuss later.

If you ever have the occasion to play with a non-composite system, bear in mind that it may not even run at standard video scan rates, which is just the situation we encounter with the PC's Monochrome Monitor.

IBM PC "Monochrome Board"

When you buy an IBM PC (or PC compatible), you must choose between two video-adapter cards: The *Color-Graphics Card* which I discuss later, or the *Monochrome* card, which displays only high-resolution text. The naming of the cards leaves something to be desired, since the Color-Graphics card can also do monochrome text. The biggest terminology problem comes, however, from the fact that the Monochrome board uses an oddball video convention and requires a special monitor.

So, if someone says they want a "monochrome monitor for an IBM PC" they might mean they want the oddball kind that goes with the Monochrome Card, or a normal monitor for use with the Color Graphics Card. And then, even though the PC's special monochrome monitor was odd when it was introduced, there are now so many that they are a kind of standard by themselves. If fact, there are several vendors making graphics cards which use the oddball monitor!

The oddball Monochrome system is actually just a variation on the ordinary systems described so far. Here are the details:

Scan Rate: 18.432 KHz (54 microseconds per line)

Lines Used for Display of Characters: 350

Vertical rate: 50 frames per second, with *no interlace*

Number of dots per line: 720 pixels

The Monochrome Card puts out 25 lines of 80 characters, each character drawn in a box which is 9 pixels wide by 14 pixels tall.

The card has a 9-pin, D-type connector (DB-9), with signals as follows:

Pin	Signal
1 and 2	Ground
3, 4, 5	Not Used
6	Intensity
7	Video
8	+ Horizontal Drive
9	− Vertical Drive

A couple of notes are in order here: The Video signal is essentially pixel on or pixel off. This is augmented by the Intensity wire which tells whether a pixel which is on is to be bright or dim.

Composite Color

Composite color uses only one cable to feed video information to the monitor. As you will have gathered if you read the previous chapter, composite-color is not very satisfactory for computer displays because of low color resolution. To add to this, if you use a television/video cassette recorder-type monitor, the image is further degraded because of built-in filters which are meant to reduce noise, but which blur the details present in computer video. In addition, such monitors have color-correction circuitry which may be a problem.

In their defense, some newer, high-quality television/video cassette recorder-type monitors do have an input for computer use which bypasses the detail-filter. However, the intrinsic color-detail problem of the composite system remains.

It is obvious that some computer manufacturers expect you to use a composite monitor, since they provide composite color output from their machine (Apple II series, for example). I must admit that I have not pursued this matter to see whether anyone is making a "for-computers-only" composite monitor. If so, it must suffer from the same technical color-detail limitations, and thus be useful only for relatively low-resolution color graphics or text.

If you are particularly interested in color graphics on a machine such as the Apple, you may want to investigate whether an RGB adapter is available.

Red-Green-Blue (RGB) Systems

This is the main color signal convention used in computers today, providing good resolution and a straightforward signal arrangement. However, even here there are numerous variations. First, let us look at the typical arrangement:

Red: A signal controlling the Red beam.

Green: A signal controlling the Green beam.

Blue: A signal controlling the Blue beam.

Horiz: A signal providing the horizontal sync, usually TTL levels.

Vert: A signal providing the vertical sync, usually TTL levels.

Variations on this can be as follows:

1. The Red, Green and Blue signals from the computer may be normal video-level signals, or they may be TTL-level digital signals which indicate pixel-on or pixel-off. If the video signals are video-level, and the computer is equipped with a fancy video section, then each color may be able to attain several different levels, permitting a fine mix of colors on the screen.

    On the other hand, more rudimentary computers may only be able to put out pixels as either on or off for each color: so, even though ordinary video levels are used, they are always at just one of two levels.

    At the monitor end, the monitor may have TTL inputs intended for use with TTL computer outputs, or it may have analog inputs. Analog inputs will respond to normal video-level signals which can then control the beams to partial intensities for each color if the computer has that ability. Finally, there may even be monitors which respond to normal video levels, but force the beams to be either on or off to improve resolution.

    It should be noted that these variations can result in a good deal of confusion since normal video levels are not that far from TTL levels. As a consequence, it is possible to get a computer with video-level outputs to drive a TTL-input monitor albeit poorly, and the reverse is true also.

2. Horizontal and vertical may be sync signals, or drive signals which are somewhat wider. They may be normally high, pulsing low, or vice versa. The nomenclature is a mess, so a signal called "positive sync" or "inverted sync" really doesn't tell you much. This is because in "normal" video, the sync component is a negative-going pulse. Is this normal or inverted? If drive signals are provided, the system is sometimes called "Direct Drive."

3. Horizontal and vertical sync signals may be combined in one wire, in which case, it looks like composite monochrome video with no video (luminance). This signal would be called *composite sync*.

4. There are some RGB systems and monitors which don't even have a sync line. Instead, the composite sync rides along with the Green. Why Green? Well, it's a long story, but if you must know....

In ordinary television-land, if you show a black-and-white movie on a color set, the major contribution of brightness is from the green beam. That is to say, white is not simply an equal contribution from all three beams. On a color picture, we can deduce that, if there is an area of brightness on the screen, probably a good portion of it is from the green beam. So we might say that, if we had to choose, the green beam is the beam most like the single beam in a monochrome system.

So, what if your computer is putting out a color signal and your color monitor breaks down? If the green signal contains the sync signals as well as the green (which is most like monochrome), all you need to do is hook up the green signal to your monochrome monitor and you have a semi-usable picture. Besides, if you carry the sync signals on the Green line, you need two less wires.

RGB Plus Intensity, The PC Color/Graphics Card

The IBM PC's Color/Graphics Card can use an RGB monitor with TTL color inputs as described earlier; however, one further embellishment is added. As you can see from the listing below, a sixth wire is added which carries Intensity to indicate whether a particular pixel is bright or dim.

Again, a DB-9 connector is used, and in a manner consistent with the Monochrome monitor, although the two monitors are not interchangeable.

Pin	Signal
1 and 2	Ground
3	Red
4	Green
5	Blue
6	Intensity
7	Not Used
8	Horizontal Drive
9	Vertical Drive

Most PC-compatible Color/Graphics Cards also have a composite output in addition (on a separate RCA phono jack). This is widely used for an ordinary single-color monitor, but may also be used for a composite color monitor. If a single-color monitor is used, and it has an analog intensity characteristic, then different colors will be displayed as different shades of grey.

15

Miscellaneous Video Tips and Hints

Types of Cable and Connectors

The type of cable used for video signals is of a construction referred to as coaxial ("coax" for short). This kind of cable is round and has a center conductor surrounded by insulation. This is surrounded, in turn, by an outer conductor, in turn surrounded by the outer insulation. The outer conductor serves two functions: it provides the ground while shielding the inner signal-carrying conductor from possible electrical noise sources.

Coaxial cable is available in many different sizes and characteristics, and there are numerous connector types, both for video and for other uses. To take the easiest path, simply buy preassembled cables of the appropriate length with the connectors already mounted. This avoids the not-insignificant aggravation of trying to mount the connectors yourself. Often they are awkward or need a special tool. However, for those who need to know . . .

Cable

Coaxial cable suitable for video use should have certain characteristics. First, it should be mechanically compatible with the connectors you propose to use. Secondly, it should have the appropriate *impedance* characteristic.

As a first step in the explanation of "impedance," it should be stated that, for higher frequency signals such as video, a coaxial cable does not merely look like a ground wire plus a signal wire. Instead, it looks like a complex mixture of capacitance between the two conductors, and inductance along the conductors.

This may not have meaning to you, but it implies that there are characteristics of the cable which will cause distortions in the signal according to the signal's voltage, and also according to whatever current may flow as a result. And the higher the frequency of the signal, the more significant the distortion.

For a particular cable, however, there is a ratio of voltage signal versus current signal, wherein the resulting distortions actually cancel each other out. The impedance number represents that ideal ratio. Now, remember that the ohm unit (already mentioned as a unit of resistance) is simply "one amp per volt." As a consequence, the very same ratio unit can be used for impedance!

It has come to pass that the ordinary video cable has an impedance characteristic of 75 ohms, which means that if we have a 1-volt signal, then it would be best to arrange for a 1/75-amp current signal to accompany it. This is done by the manufacturers in designing video outputs and inputs. The importance to us is that now we have equipment which expects 75-ohm cable, so that is what we should obtain.

There are some more-complicated phenomena going on in the cable, but they all lead to the conclusion that we want to use 75-ohm cable, with a 75-ohm monitor input and a 75-ohm computer output.

If 75-ohm cable is *not* used, then expect some degradation of the signal to occur. As I mentioned above, the distortions are more significant at higher frequencies, which corresponds to the high-detail elements of a video image. So, expect to see a reduction in crispness with non-75-ohm cables. You can, however, get away with almost any kind of wiring for *temporary* use.

Connectors

There are at least three kinds of connectors in common use for computer video, these are the RCA Phono connector, the BNC connector, and the "@ # $ % 8-pin job." These are pictured in Figure 15-1. Actually, the 8-pin rectangular connector is sometimes described as an "I" connector, although I have never personally met anyone who knew that. If you ever have to buy one, try the service departments of large video stores (video cassette recorder-type places).

Note that if your video gear uses the RCA-phono connector, you might be tempted to use audio cables. These will work; however, you may see an improvement using genuine 75-ohm cables intended for video use.

> **Valuable-hint-of-the-page:**   If you need BNC cables, buy them already assembled. BNC connector parts are *very* dependent on the kind of cable you use, and generally require special tools.

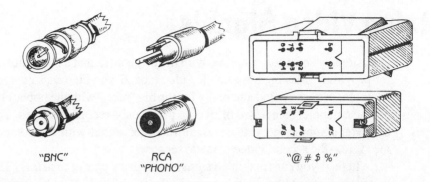

"BNC"   RCA
              "PHONO"   "@ # $ %"

Figure 15-1   Three types of video connector in common use, showing male and female of each.

Tapping Off Video to Two Monitors

Frequently, it is desired to send the computer's video signal to two or more different monitors. In a pinch, this can be done simply by obtaining a "Y" adapter cable (or cables) with appropriate connectors. However, be prepared for the possibility that the resulting pictures will be reduced in detail, contrast and brightness. In extreme cases, you may even lose sync. If you were following the impedance discussion, you will recognize this as a case where the 75-ohm computer output is feeding two 75-ohm inputs, which, as a result, look like only 37.5 ohms. This results in a smaller signal, possibly inadequate for a monitor.

If you need to feed your video signal to multiple monitors, you may need to obtain a *video enhancer* box, which is an inexpensive gadget used to amplify video signals and adjust the way they look. You can insert this between the computer and your "Y" adapter cable.

Recording Computer Video

If you have any ideas about recording your computer's video on a video cassette recorder, test it out to make sure you get sufficient resolution. You may even have trouble getting the video cassette recorder to sync to the computer signal.

To record the computer signal at all, it will need to be composite video. And, of course, all of the previous discussions about lack-luster resolution in composite video will apply here also. So again, try it out before you are committed to recording computer video output.

Mixing Video Signals

Occasionally someone comes up with the bright idea that a computer could be ideal for providing titles on home-made video tape. Two video cassette recorders and a computer are assembled and ready for the big "mix," with the hopes of superimposing the computer-generated titles onto previously-recorded scenes. The question is how you combine the video cassette recorder signal with the computer signal to feed it into the second video cassette recorder.

In fact, you can mix video signals with just a pair of resistors. The problem is that for a proper video signal to result, the two signals must be synchronized! It is no use if, at a certain instant, Signal A is working on the bottom left of its picture, while Signal B is at the middle right! Unfortunately, you have no means by which to synchronize your video cassette recorder and computer together. So, basically, forget it!

There are, however, dedicated small computers with syncing capability which will do titling. Recently I saw one from Sony, and another one which was a modified Apple. This is not the sort of thing which you can reasonably expect your average computer to do, however, unless the capability is specifically designed in by the manufacturer.

Use of Video Projectors

Teachers, college professors, and anyone who wants to use a computer in front of a large audience is interested in what can be done with video projectors.

If you attempt to use an entertainment-type video projector, you run up against all of the previously mentioned problems with using televisions with computers: low resolution and poor color. Add to this the problem that projection-televisions produce even poorer resolution, and you have a class full of headaches.

More expensive video-projectors are available which have RGB inputs. However, these units still do not have tremendous resolution—80 column displays are only marginally comfortable, and the convergence of the three beams is not very good. As you know by now, any deficiency in the ability to display details is accentuated by the nature of computer video. For the best results in displaying text, use only one beam (either green or red).

Instability

With all of the computer-to-monitor cabling possibilities, you would think that if you got the cabling correct, your troubles would be over. Sometimes the monitor does not work properly at first, but it is merely a case of adjusting the horizontal and vertical hold, and perhaps the size controls.

Nonetheless, there are certain computers whose signals deviate enough from what could be considered as standard that certain monitors will not run properly with them. A possible problem area is in the width of sync pulses.

This is the case with the Zenith Z-150 for example, a PC clone, which is rather choosy about which monitors it will drive. A modification is available however, which will solve this. Models of this machine we have seen had a vertical sync which did not incorporate inverted horizontal syncs, and the overall width of the vertical sync pulse appears to be non-standard.

Wavy or Blotchy Screen

Here's a symptom which pops up with some regularity on just-purchased systems, particularly when the user has to assemble his own video cable. The symptom is that the video looks normal most of the time. However, with particular patterns of text, particularly long lines, a kink develops. Some lines of text may be displaced horizontally, or a bright blotch appears, usually from the left of the screen. Characteristically, the defect moves up the screen as the text is scrolled.

Before checking anything else, check to see that you have hooked up the ground on the video cable correctly. On some machines using multi-pin connectors (perhaps a creative use of a DIN connector) there may be *two* ground pins, which causes some confusion. One pin is the signal ground (that's the one you want), and the other is the chassis ground.

Video Input Devices

There are sophisticated boards which allow you to *input* pictures to your computer and to save them on disk. While I will not cover the subject in depths, a few words are appropriate.

There are two classes of video-input devices. The inexpensive kind generally does not use a real video camera. Instead, it uses a light-sensing array chip, often just a specially selected, ordinary memory chip with a window in the lid. This chip is usually mounted in a cheap camera body, and has a cable to a board in the computer. This class of device is typically monochrome, low resolution, and may be slow. It probably uses the computer's own graphics capability for display. Since this type of video input device does not actually require you to mess with video signals personally, I don't have anything more to say about it.

The expensive video input device is usually termed a *frame grabber*, and can cost more than the computers for which it is an accessory. It can generally use a real video camera, or indeed, almost any video signal. If you are interested in this kind of equipment, you probably will invest quite some time in studying each model. However, here is a warning about a very important pitfall.

Be very careful about exactly what kind of video signals such a unit can accept. These units are especially sensitive to sync problems. The brochure may say "accepts standard video signals" or "RS-170 video," and it is up to you to make sure your equipment supplies just that. In particular, VHS and Beta video cassette recorders often will not work with such a board, and they cause problems *especially* if used in PAUSE mode. This is because, in PAUSE mode, video cassette recorders put out a video signal which is not very steady. Most monitors can follow this unsteadiness, but frame-grabbers may not be able to. Some frame grabbers have circuitry described as "Gen-Lock," and while this may sound promising, it does not solve the problem.

The video cassette recorder problem is important when you wish to use the frame grabber for detailed, frame-by-frame analysis of data gathered on a video cassette recorder perhaps sports plays or, microscope sessions. Remember that you can really grab only one frame at a time, because it takes up so much space that after that one frame, you either have to analyze it or take time and space to store it on disk. So ideally, you would like to be able to grab and analyze frame by frame, by having the video cassette recorder in pause and advancing frame by frame each time the computer is ready. This is exactly the hardest video signal for a grabber to work with.

So, if you are considering purchase of a video grabber board, make sure it will work in the situations you have in mind!

Converting Television Sets to Video Monitors

I once wrote a magazine article on how to convert televisions to video monitors. Now I say, don't bother. There is an element of danger to it, both to you and your computer, it is technically tricky in some respects, and the resulting monitor is of low resolution. There are now cheap commercial monitors available. If you are smart enough to modify a television set, then you are probably also "rich" enough to just buy a monitor, and are certainly smart enough to observe that it works better and more safely.

16

Power Connections

Why Are You Here?

There are three good possibilities as to why you might read this section. The first is that you always read books from cover to cover. The second is that you want to know if there is something you should be doing to protect your expensive investment. And finally, the third possibility is that your computer bombs out intermittently for no good reason.

So far as protection goes, read on with the idea that, unless power problems are widely known in your area, you probably don't need to worry.

If you've been having intermittent problems, I'm sorry to tell you that they may be caused by power problems, or they may be caused by some other hardware problem or software bug. In my opinion, more computer problems have been erroneously ascribed to power problems than to any other source.

The major topics of interest which we will cover are as follows:

- Worries about protection of equipment.

- Rumors that intermittent failures are due to "bad power."

- Safety considerations

- Some intermittent-problem repairs you can do yourself.

Terminology

First let's establish a name for the electricity available at a wall socket. I'm going to use the term *line power*, commonly designated as 115 volts AC. The cable on an appliance, lamp or computer that plugs into the wall is called the *line cord*.

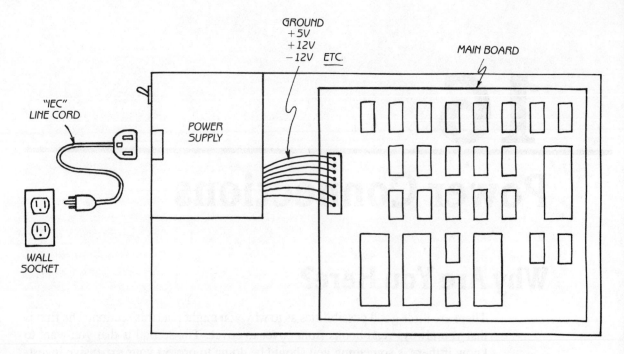

Figure 16-1 This diagram shows the principal players in the theatre of power supply. Power comes originally from the wall socket. It is brought to the equipment via a line cord, which is shown here as an IEC type. The Power Supply is the part of the equipment which converts the line power to a form which the computer can use. In this case, 5 volts, 12 volts and −12 volts are shown.

If the line cord is detachable, then there is a connector where the cord plugs into the equipment, and this connector may be one of several types. The connector on the equipment is always male (has pins) and that on the cord is female (this arrangement being necessary for safety, of course). On newer equipment, the line cord-to-equipment connector is a standard three-conductor type referred to as an *IEC power line connector* (IEC is the International Electro-Technical Commission). In North America, the wall-socket end of an IEC line cord is equipped with a suitable three-pin plug (Figure 16-1).

Inside most pieces of electronic equipment is a section called the *power supply*. This is really a power *converter*, converting line power into the form needed by the electronic components.

For most of this chapter, I will assume that the equipment we are dealing with is a typical personal computer, or its printer, modem or other accessories which receives power via a line cord which plugs into a wall socket. For ease of writing, I'll talk about computers only; but everything also applies to printers and terminals and other devices as well.

Problems Caused by Improper Supply of Power

Except for those occasions when you forget to plug into the wall socket, electrical supply troubles are of the worst kind. The difficulty is that supply problems are often intermittent, occurring from once a minute to once a month, and can be responsible for failure of any aspect of your computer's operation.

As a consequence, it is tempting to blame almost any type of computer failure on line power problems.

In tracking down intermittent problems, the key thing is to put on your detective hat and note *anything* which might be a common factor in the failures. If necessary, take your machine to another location with a different supply of power. Try to bring another machine of the same type to your problem location. Use different software. Note what kind of weather is involved, if you were operating your air conditioner or what other equipment was on when the problem occurred.

For what it's worth, in my opinion, almost *no* problems in post-1980 machines are related to bad line power. Those problems which *do* stem from bad power are easily verified by operating in a different location for a while. However, don't be too convinced when operating in a new location causes the problem to go away. It might simply be that you have shaken up an intermittent connection inside the computer, and it will now work for a while. Relocate back and forth a few times to

On the other hand, there are reasonable numbers of intermittent failures attributable to defects in the power supply unit inside the computer, probably in proportion to the number of square inches it takes up relative to the rest of the electronics (more on this subject later).

The following section is for those readers wishing more background on line power and its ailments. Following that is a section with miscellaneous hints and tips on power-related subjects.

Laundering the Power

It turns out that power which is supplied to all the chips in your computer has to be quite clean. If it's not, it can upset their operation, which will result in anything from a slight error to actual damage requiring repair. Still, even a slight error isn't slight if it's in somebody's pay check!

Obviously, it is of great importance to make sure that the power is clean, and manufacturers of various power-line accessories are very eager to supply us with solutions for the potential problems. In the next chapter, I'll describe the various problems which can plague your computer's power department, and what solutions are available for them. First, more about the power that comes out of a wall socket and about power supplies.

At Your Wall Socket . . .

Most readers probably realize that somewhere, far away, there is a power-generating station where you send in money and they convert it into electricity. Electrical power is fed into large wires running either underground or above the ground on pylons or towers to your neighborhood. There, local distribution stations convert the power for local distribution over smaller cables which come to your block (more or less). There, another conversion is made into the form which is suitable to feed your house or office. The electricity is fed through your fuse box or circuit breakers, and finally into the building wiring through which it is brought to the wall sockets in each room in the form known (in North America) as "115-volts AC" or "110-volts AC" (these are only nominal figures).

I glossed over "form" and "conversion" a bit. By "form" I meant voltage, and by conversion I meant change in voltage, and these will need a little explaining, as does "AC."

It is terribly unfortunate for writers, such as myself, that electric power arrives as "AC," because it takes a whole lot more explaining than "DC," so please bear with me. It'll be worth it, if it makes you more knowledgeable than ordinary computer salesmen, right?

All About AC

If you were following along in Chapter 2 regarding electricity, then you were already exposed to the way a battery works. To summarize, in the case of a battery powering a lamp, the battery voltage (a "pushing force") causes a substance we call "charge" to flow along the wires through the lamp. The rate of charge flow is called "current" (amount of charge per second). The lamp has a characteristic called "resistance," which restricts the flow of charge (and hence the current) and is what stops all of the charge in the battery from immediately flowing through the bulb, thereby depleting the battery. Most explanations leave out the idea of charge and talk only about voltage and current, but I believe that the idea of charge is helpful.

Charge flows in only one direction all the time, from the plus terminal of the battery to the minus. This setup long ago acquired the name "Direct Current," or DC. A better name would be "uni-directional current" or, better still, "constant-polarity voltage," since it is the voltage which causes the direction of the current, and that is arranged by the two "poles" of the battery, which are stationary. Anyway, we are stuck with "DC."

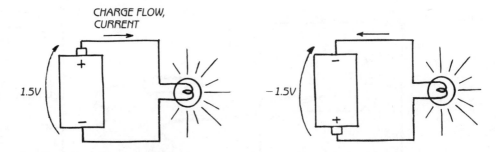

Figure 16-2 A battery will power a lamp whichever way around it is connected.

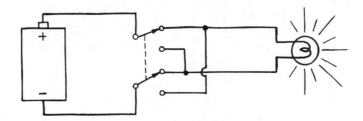

Figure 16-3 The lamp continues to work even if we continually reverse the battery very rapidly.

You would think that it would be quite convenient if wall sockets simply operated like batteries. They do not, however, and there is a very good reason.

Let us again consider the battery powering the lamp, but, in this case, the battery is reversed. To be sure, the charge would flow in the opposite direction, but the lamp would still glow. This is shown in Figure 16-2. Suppose, now, that we arranged a switch so that we could reverse the battery by flipping the switch. The lamp will glow no matter what the position of the switch. Even if we flip the switch back and forth very quickly, so that there is never an instant when the battery is disconnected, the lamp will still glow. This is illustrated in Figure 16-3. The charge will reverse direction so quicky that it will cause no problems at all.

The arrangement I've just described is a form of *Alternating Current*. The lamp still operates very adequately from this AC, and, as it turns out, so do many other appliances, such as heaters, stoves, and toasters. Many other appliances are just as easily built to run on AC, such as those with electric motors, like vacuum cleaners, fans, electric drills and so on.

The switched-battery AC which I've just described is not quite the same as the wall socket. What I've described switches sharply between full voltage one way and full voltage the other way, applied across the lamp. The wall socket variety of AC turns gradually from positive full voltage to negative full voltage; in fact, a graph of the voltage would show a sine wave. The alternation takes place at 60 times a second (in North America). This 60 cycle-per second (60 hertz) sine-wave is very convenient for the utility company's power generators to produce.

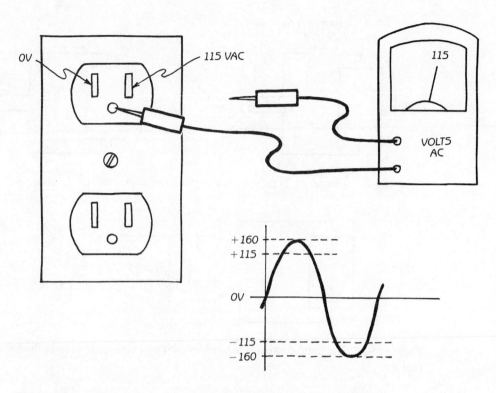

Figure 16-4   Here are the voltages you would measure at a wall socket.

Figure 16-4 shows the voltages that you would measure at a wall socket. The smaller flat pin is the "hot" one, and will measure 115-volts AC. The actual waveform which would be seen on an oscilloscope is shown in Figure 16-4. Notice that although this is called "115 volts" the peaks are actually at ±160 volts. The 115-volt figure is said to be the Root Mean Square (RMS) value. It is a method of averaging the peaks and troughs in the waveform, so that 115 volts AC (RMS) provides the same power (to a lamp for example) as 115 volt DC.

You may have been imagining that our battery and lamp were perhaps an innocuous "D" cell hooked up to a flashlight battery. Such a battery possesses a voltage of only 1.5 volts, which will not do you any harm. In comparison, the wall socket carries 115 volts, and is *dangerous* to handle.

Why AC?

You may recall that electrical power is equal to voltage multiplied by current. Electrical power is measured in watts; one watt is the power obtained from one volt at one amp of current. The familiar, mechanical-power quantity of one horsepower is equal to about 747 watts.

The quantity of "power" is the quantity in which we are ultimately interested because it represents the rate of doing work. Applied to an electric motor, it tells how quickly the electric saw will cut, or how fast the electric mixer will beat the cake mix. Applied to a heater, it tells how much heat will be generated per unit of time. Keep in mind that, so far as the work is concerned, we are really uninterested in the voltage and current individually, but we are very interested in their product (multiplication), namely power.

Consequently, in a particular application we will have a need for a particular amount of power. Then if we have a high voltage we need a low current, and vice versa.

The exciting aspect of AC is that it can be used with a *transformer*. A transformer is a gadget which allows you to apply one AC voltage to a pair of wires on one side (called the *primary winding*), and get out a different AC voltage across two wires on the other side (called the *secondary winding*). Correspondingly, the primary and secondary currents will also be different.

For a particular amount of power being drawn from a transformer, you will find that the power coming out of the transformer equals the power going into it. (There actually are some losses, which show up as heat, but we'll ignore that confusion here.)

As an example, suppose we have a transformer whose input is 100 volts AC, and whose output is 10 volts AC. If we connect a load whose resistance is 1 ohm, then 10 amps will be drawn from the secondary winding. The power is 10 volts multiplied by 10 amps to equal 100 watts. Similarly, the power going into the transformer must be 100 watts. Since the input voltage is 100 volts, the input current must be 1 amp.

As you can see, for a particular amount of power, not only does the transformer give us a voltage conversion, it also converts the current being drawn.

Thus the transformer is a tool for permitting us to draw the desired power, but allows us to choose the combination of voltage and current most appropriate for our needs.

AC for Power Distribution

The transformer is very useful in helping to distribute power from the power station.

If you operate a 1-horsepower electric motor (and suppose it was 100% efficient, which is not realistic) then you need 747 watts of electric power to run it at full load. If you had a choice, you could ask for 1 amp at 747 volts, or you could ask for 747 amps at 1 volt. Or you could ask for 1/10 amp at 7470 volts, or most likely, 6.5 amps at 115 volts. You would have to select 1-horsepower motors designed for each of these combinations.

There are some tradeoffs in this decision. If you picked the 747-amp choice, you would need huge wires to carry the current without melting. Wires get hot because they have some small resistance, and heat is generated by forcing current through such a resistance. The thicker the wire, the lower the resistance.

If you picked the 7470-volt choice, then the wires could be very thin, needing to carry only 100 milliamps. However, the insulation would need to be very thick to avoid arcing due to the high voltage. Arcing occurs when the voltage between two nearby wires is so high that charge jumps across through the air or even burns through insulation.

What all this tells us is that, in fact, 115 volts was picked as a voltage which is low enough so that the arcing is not a problem, but high enough so that the current required for typical household gadgets is low enough to be carried on reasonably sized wires.

However, if you added all of the demands of your neighbors or office mates to your own, that adds up to a very large current at 115 volts, needing cables which would be very heavy and expensive to run all the way to Niagara Falls. The solution is provided by the transformer!

The utility company carries power over long distances at a very high voltage (perhaps 100,000 volts). At your neighboorhood distribution station it is fed into a transformer and comes out at around 12,000 volts. Close to your house it is converted to 115 volts. If you plug in a 100-watt lamp, you draw almost an amp. But that takes only about 8 milliamp at 12,000 volts, and 1 milliamp at 100,000 volts!

So, you can see that by carrying electrical power at high voltages the utility company saves a great deal on very expensive wire, and the towers which carry it.

AC for Convenient Domestic Use

Just as the transformer is useful to the utility company for converting to different voltages during distribution, so it is also useful inside domestic appliances which often need quite low voltages for powering their internal circuitry. A stereo receiver might need a 40-volt supply, for example. A computer needs a 5-volt supply. But there's a catch, the receiver, the computer and most other *electronic* equipment needs a DC supply, just like a battery. In other words, although a lamp or heater would be equally happy on AC or DC, the radio or internal works of a computer must have DC.

DC from AC

The conversion of the 115-volt line power to DC at voltages convenient for electronics is the job of the power supply, although, of course, it is really a power converter.

Ok, I've finished with the explanation of what the utility company is up to, and why we have AC, and we're finally back to discussing the power supply inside the computer. This is the critical element about which we need to know in order to decide whether or not we need to feed it specially treated electricity, and when line power problems might cause troubles.

So, let's look at what the power supply does. In a simple design, the 115-volt AC is fed into a transformer, and out of which comes a much lower voltage. This is then "rectified and smoothed" as the description usually goes. This means it's converted from fully reversing voltage (swings negative and positive) to pulsating positive by a device called a *rectifier*. The pulsations are then smoothed out by a device called a *capacitor*, and a large device at that. The capacitor functions as a sort of charge reservoir, or to look at it another way, as a short-term, rechargeable battery. The pulses from the rectifier charge it up, while the load, in this case the computer circuits causes a continuous drain. Figure 16-5a shows the simplest sort of DC power supply possible. The transformer provides the voltage we need. The rectifier or "diode" marked "D" is a component which permits current to flow only one way, so that only positive pulses are released at one per 60th of a second. By using a transformer with a *center-tap*, and an extra diode, we can obtain a pulse for every positive and negative peak of the sine-wave, as shown in Figure 16-5b. In Figure 16-5c the capacitor C acts as a short-term reservoir. Each of the pulses shown for Figure 16-5b "tops up" the capacitor. Between pulses, current to the circuit drains the voltage slightly. This fluctuation is referred to as *ripple*. The lower the supply current, or the larger the capacitor value (measured in microfarads), the less the ripple. Humming of aging stereo sets is sometimes due to failing supply capacitors, especially if the humming is at 120 hertz!

At this stage, the power is more or less similar to what would come out of a battery, except that the voltage is not accurately fixed. In fact, the voltage will vary depending upon what the utility company is supplying as input today. If the nominal output is 8 volts for an input of 115 volts, then you might get 8.6 volts if the utility supplies 125 volts, or you will drop to only 7.4 volts or so if everyone in town turns on the air conditioning and the utility can only manage a meager 105 volts.

The chips in the computer are quite picky about the voltage they run on. Most want 5.0 volts, give or take 0.25 volt. For this reason, the raw DC power is fed into a regulator circuit where it is trimmed down to exactly 5 volts. A feedback arrangement monitors the 5 volts and continually adjusts it to compensate for variations in the load that the chips are drawing, or for fluctuations in the utility supply.

Figure 16-6a shows a supply which includes a voltage regulator. The regulator might be a single-component, three-terminal regulator, or be built from multiple discrete components. In either case, the principle is the same. Figure 16-6b shows the inside of the regulator, where the output voltage is adjusted by

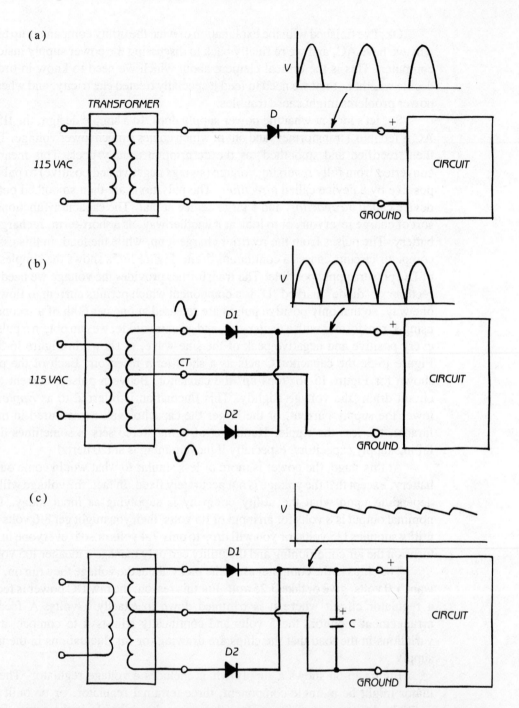

Figure 16-5   (a) Shows the simplest sort of DC power supply possible. (b) Shows pulse for every positive and negative peak of the sine-wave. (c) Capacitor C acting as a short-term reservoir.

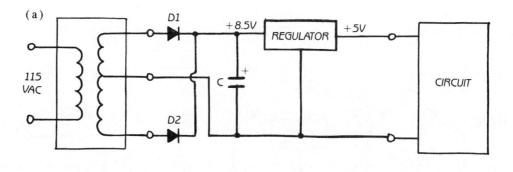

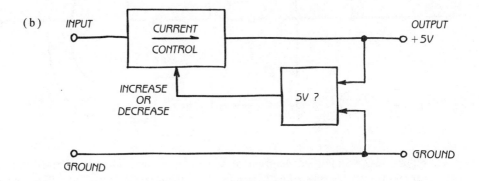

Figure 16-6   The power supply shown includes a voltage regulator (a); the interior of the regulator is also shown (b).

regulating the current. The less the current is restricted, the higher the output voltage. However, the output voltage is continuously being checked to see if it is 5 volts. If it is slightly above or below, the current regulation is adjusted to bring it closer.

It should be pointed out that this regulation process involves essentially giving away the excess power as heat. If the regulator is putting out 5 volts at 10 amps, and the regulator input is 8 volts, then there is 3 volts multiplied by 10 amps which equals 30 watts given off as heat, not an insignificant consideration. And imagine what happens if the line voltage goes up, raising the regulator input voltage!

By the way, a power supply such as the one I've been describing is called a *linear supply*, and isn't used in many computers any more, although it *is* used inside stereos and other less-intelligent electronic devices. It was widely used in early computers up to S-100 units and LSI-11s. It has been largely superseded in more modern machines by what is called a *switching supply*.

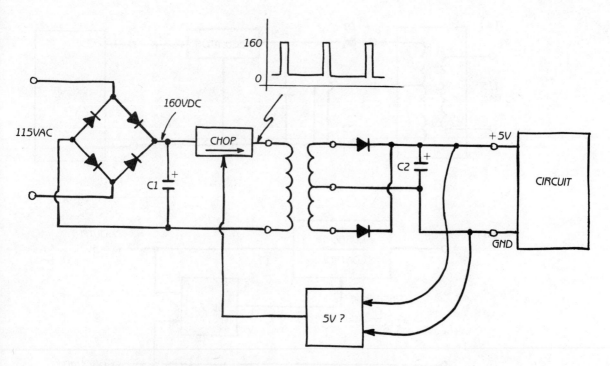

Figure 16-7 Simplified diagram of switching supply. The transformer and the two capacitors can be substantially smaller than their counterparts in a linear supply. In addition, far less heat is generated.

The Switcher

A major problem in linear power supplies occurs because the transformer required is obnoxiously bulky. It turns out that transformer size and weight is related to how much power will be drawn from its output and also to the alternation frequency. A designer can do little about how much current the computer circuitry will draw. And on the surface, it would seem like the designer can't do anything about the 60 hertz AC frequency either.

Not so! A clever design of power supply is replacing linears in many applications. The basis of this supply is to take the incoming 115 volts and rectify and smooth that directly. This provides around 160 or 320 volts, depending on the circuit used. Then some electronics switches this DC voltage very rapidly, creating an AC voltage at about 20,000 to 30,000 alternations per second.

This is fed into a transformer, which can be much smaller due to the higher frequency of operation. The output from this transformer is then rectified and smoothed. There is regulation by monitoring the output voltage and sending a corrective feedback signal to the input switching circuit. The Switcher is shown in Figure 16-7.

This kind of power supply is more complicated, but the actual space and weight taken is far less because of the saving in transformer size, and in the size of the capacitors used for smoothing at each stage. In addition, much less heat is generated than in the linear design.

As examples, the Apple II series, the Macintosh, the IBM PC and many other computers have switching supplies.

17

Power Ailments

There are several line power maladies which could plague your equipment. These include:

- Line voltage failure ("black out").
- Low line voltage ("brown out").
- High line voltage ("blew out"… sorry, got carried away)
- Line noise.
- Line surge.

For serious troubleshooting, you really need to know what is happening on the line. You could hook up an oscilloscope (be careful about voltage settings!) and then sit there staring at it endlessly. Obviously not an optimal solution, particularly since the phenomena you are looking for are non-repetitive.

If you have some money at your disposal, you can rent or even buy what is called a line monitor. This instrument is intended to do your scope-sitting for you. You can set various parameters, such as low-voltage and high-voltage points, and the instrument provides a periodic printout of what the voltage was, and will print a report on any occasion when the low or high points were violated.

Line Noise and Line Surges

These two items are probably the line problems which are most talked about. *Line noise* is not something you can hear. Rather, it refers to extraneous fluctuations in the 60-hertz, 115-volt sine wave that is coming out of the wall socket. These may result from someone nearby operating certain kinds of electric motors, or other appliances. "Nearby" in this case means from a related electrical line.

Line surges, also called *transients*, are a particular variety of noise, namely very big voltage *spikes*, short pulses measured in microseconds (millionths of seconds) but thousands of volts. These may be the result of a lightning strike on a power line, or nearby operation of industrial-sized electrical equipment.

There is a solution for each of these two problems: a *noise filter* for noise, and a *surge suppressor* for the spikes. As a raw component, a noise filter looks like a small box the size of a matchbox, with two 115-volt AC input wires and two 115-volt AC output wires. On some units, the input wires are actually a socket for an IEC line cord. It works in very much the same way as an audio filter for your stereo (like a tone control or section of an equalizer). It permits 60-hertz signals to pass through, but blocks high frequencies, typically in the range of 150 kilohertz to 30 megahertz.

The suppressor is actually a component with various names such as *surgistor*, or *Metal-Oxide Varistor (MOV)* and looks like a disk the size of a half-dollar with two wires. It is wired across the 115-volt AC wires. The device usually just sits there doing nothing. However, if a voltage spike comes along which exceeds the device's threshold voltage, it suddenly conducts, not allowing the voltage to exceed the threshold. The threshold voltage is also called the *clamping voltage*.

When this happens, the current in the surgistor will be quite high, perhaps in the thousands of amps, depending on the source of the spike and how strongly the energy was delivered to the electrical system. The surgistor's ratings are in volts for threshold, and in joules for energy absorption ability. A *joule* is equal to a watt of power for one second. Thus a 200-volt, 10-joule surgistor could absorb a 1,000 amp pulse of current for 5 microseconds.

$$1000 \text{ A} \times 200 \text{ V} \times 5 \text{ us} = 10 \text{ J}$$

Suppressors and filters are often packaged and sold as separate gadgets for your computer. Sometimes they are incorporated into plug-strips sold for computer use.

You may wonder if you *really need* these devices. It's the old story of selling insurance. You may never need it, but do you want to take the risk? Well, I'm tired of this sort of sales pitch and I don't feel the risk is that great.

Nowadays, computers and their peripherals are considered consumer items, and are treated by most users just like stereos or other electronic gear. As a result, users plug their computers into any available wall socket, octupus plug, or extension cord, and expect it to run. If the computer breaks down, even because of crummy power, the manufacturer picks up the tab in warranty repairs and lost reputation, and those costs are *very* expensive. So the computer manufacturer is very interested in making sure that his computer is insensitive to poor power, and already possesses reasonable protection.

In addition, almost *no* computer manufacturers build their own power supplies. They just buy them from a power-supply manufacturer who has experience in switchers, cranks them out by the tens of thousands, purchases components in the hundreds of thousands or millions, and has obtained the requisite UL certifications. These power-supply manufacturers are competing heavily for business, and their prices are pretty uniform.

So, a computer manufacturer can shop around for what he considers to be a good power supply—one that is reliable, and one that will stand up to most power-line problems. The computer manufacturer is inclined to get a good power supply, has a choice of good designs, and has motivation to spend a little extra on the power supply if necessary.

In printers, the situation is different in that the power supply is generally built by the printer manufacturer. However, there is still plenty of motivation for the manufacturer to include protection as a matter of course, and this is borne out in contemporary printers. In any case, it is nowhere near such a disaster for a printer to hiccup as it is for a computer.

So, I say, be daring. For contemporary machines, forget the external surge suppressors and noise filters. That is, unless, you have some extraordinary conditions . . .

Extraordinary Conditions

There are a couple of extraordinary situations which should sound a little alarm regarding protection of equipment. These situations include operation in an area affected by switching of the source of line power (including frequent power outages), and operation in industrial conditions in the vicinity of heavy machinery.

Power Source Switched: Examples of this would be buildings which periodically switch to emergency power (hospitals for example) or which are operated part time from a co-generation facility (have their own individual power station). When the alternate source of power is switched in, a large surge may occur.

Industrial Machinery: Similarly, heavy machinery means surges in the demand for power, which will cause wild fluctuations as the supply tries to keep up. In addition, many types of machinery store energy, and, under certain conditions, will release it back into the line in the form of a surge. A large motor, for example, will continue to turn for some time after power is disconnected. After disconnection, any motor then becomes a generator. At the instant following the opening of the switch (to turn off the motor), the motor may generate quite a high voltage which arcs across the slightly open switch causing a spike on the line.

Black Out

How long will a computer run if there's a complete power failure? This is governed by how long the computer's smoothing capacitors will hold up the supply voltage, which is typically one to two cycles (of 60 hertz) or 16 to 33 milliseconds. So, a computer will not hold up long enough to save your files!

If your computer *must* keep running in the case of a black out (or if you experience a lot of them), then you might want to investigate an *uninterruptible power supply* (UPS). These boxes run in the $500- to $1000- range for modest sized units, available from computer and computer-supply retailers. Your computer plugs into the UPS and the UPS plugs into the wall. The UPS has internal batteries from which it can generate synthetic 115-volts AC in case of a power outage. Different capacities are available, depending on how long the UPS must be able to run without line power.

Low Line Voltage

It is apparently not unusual for some metropolitan areas to experience "brown outs" particularly in the peak of summer when there is a heavy electrical load due to air-conditioning. This might cause line voltage to drop to perhaps 95 volts AC, and occasionally lower. This will adversely affect the linear power supply, but probably not the switcher.

In the case of heavy duty linear supplies (used in some big computers and printers) it is necessary that they be designed "close to the edge," that is, with little tolerance for low voltage. If they could tolerate low voltage well, then under *normal* circumstances they would be giving off unnecessarily large quantities of heat. To permit adjustment close to the edge, many linear supplies come with an internal switch or jumper wire to select operation for normal local conditions of (for example) 105 volts, 115 volts or 125 volts. Different connections to the transformer are used. This is not intended to be adjusted on a daily basis, but it does show how choosy such linear supplies can be.

The switcher by comparison might operate over the range 90 to 135-volts AC quite happily.

If you suspect a problem with low voltage, this is quite easy to check with an inexpensive voltmeter. Be sure to set the meter to AC volts on an appropriate scale, and use proper caution when probing AC sockets (one hand in pocket). For a three-hole socket, the round hole is ground, the larger flat hole is neutral (approximately zero volts relative to ground), and the smaller flat hole is the hot one. Of course, there is always the possibility that the socket was wired wrongly.

If line voltage does turn out to be a problem, and your equipment has either a linear supply or has a switcher that can't handle the dips, then help is available in the form of a *constant voltage transformer*, or CVT. This device is also referred to as a *saturated core* or *resonant transformer*, names which refer to aspects of its operation. Unlike ordinary transformers, this unit puts out a constant 115 volts AC for any input within a wide range.

Constant voltage transformers are available as raw transformers, or as packaged units with line cord and sockets. In this latter form they may go by the name *power conditioner*.

By the way, a small proportion of linear power supplies already employ the CVT design in their transformer, so it would be worth checking this before acquiring an additional CVT.

Also, CVTs do a good job in getting rid of spikes and other line noise. This is useful to know if you had any doubt as to whether noise filters and suppressors are needed in addition to a CVT.

High Line Voltage

Line voltage generally has to be quite high (130 to 135 volts) before any major problems result. Such a voltage will definitely be problematic for a heavily-loaded linear power supply. Even 125 volts will be hot if the linear supply is set up to expect 105 volts. A switcher or CVT design will cope much better.

Again, a meter can be used to test for this condition. If it turns out to be a difficulty, a rare occurrence, then again, a CVT may be in order. If you are in an office situation, it may be possible to contact your building manager and see about getting the voltage adjusted at the local distribution transformer.

I cannot resist telling the story of a particular suspected high-voltage problem. This involved a printer which failed about once a day, and which was on service contract with a major three-initial company. For those not familiar with three-initial service contracts, the customer is responsible for absolutely pristine conditions in every respect before any blame can be laid at the feet of the three initials. At any rate, I became involved in mediating this dispute which had raged for about a year.

The three initials had discovered that the local line voltage in this large office building was high (about 128 volts). This exceeded the specs in the book for the power supply, they claimed, and therefore the power supply was acting up. Four three-piece suits were dispatched to tell the customer to either fix the line voltage or the three initials would have to take *all* of their equipment off contract!

Having three initials myself, I figured I would test the power supply and find out if it, indeed, had any problems at 128 volts. This is very naughty if there is a service contract. It turned out that the printer had a different model of supply than what was shown in the specs, and was quite happy from 90 volts to 140 volts! Such a test can be performed with a variable transformer, a well known brand being Variac.

I contacted one of the more-affable suits and suggested another look. Shortly, it was discovered that the failures were due to a loose screw in the printhead which was sometimes detected by the built-in microprocessor which would then shut down the operation. Loud silence from the suits and a good example of how power problems can be so misleading.

Miscellaneous Hints and Tips

Safety, Three-Wire Cords, Etc.

Most computer equipment comes with a three-wire line cord, and that is the way it should stay unless you are daring or foolhardy. Let's look at the point of having a three wire cord in the first place.

In order to deliver power at all, two wires are required. In the 115-volt AC case, one wire is neutral and the other is hot. If you connected a voltmeter (set to AC-volts) between the neutral and the ground (a water pipe for example) it would read close to zero. If you performed the same test on the hot wire, the meter would read around 115 volts.

Those two wires go inside each appliance, lamp, hand tool, computer and so on. Of particular concern is what happens if there is a malfunction in the equipment. A representative worst-case scenario would be for the hot wire to come loose and contact somewhere it's not supposed to touch. If the equipment has a metal case, the hot wire might touch that metal case. If you happen to touch the case or any metal part of the equipment (fairly likely), and you are also somehow connected to ground (by touching a faucet, standing barefoot on concrete, or many other ways) you will receive a severe shock, possibly a fatal one.

The solution is simple. All that is necessary is to connect a ground wire to the metal case on the equipment. This guarantees that, if the above scenario was to take place, the case would still be grounded, and the equipment would momentarily draw a large current until a fuse or circuit breaker blows.

Regulations were then imposed requiring ground wires to be attached to most equipment. This ground is supplied through the third hole on the wall socket, and is carried to your equipment via the third wire in the line cord. And, of course, the widespread grounding of equipment means that there are all the more grounded objects that you could come in contact with which would be dangerous in the above scenario of the ungrounded box and the broken hot wire!

All of this tells us that we should not defeat the three-wire system by using two-wire adaptor plugs *unless* the third lug on the adaptor plug is indeed screwed to the wall plate like it is supposed to be. However, even this may not be sufficient. It is not uncommon to find an ungrounded two-pin wall box.

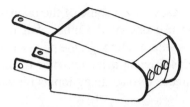

Figure 17-1 This handy gadget plugs into a three-pin socket and indicates whether the socket has been wired correctly and whether the wiring is still intact.

You may thus be interested in an inexpensive, handy test gadget which is available at hardware stores and electronics emporiums. This device looks like a three-pin plug and has three small lights on it (see Figure 17-1). When you plug this device into a wall socket, or into an adaptor plug, it immediately tells you whether all has been wired correctly and safely.

Sufficient Power for Adding Boards

In machines where there are slots available for adding accessory boards, it is worthwhile to allow for a period of caution following installation of a new board, especially if the slots are close to full. Make extra back-ups until you are confident all is well.

There are a couple of possibilities as to what might happen if you have insufficient power. One possibility is that the machine will limp along on a low voltage. This is annoying because if the voltage gets low enough, perhaps 4.7 volts instead of 5 volts, then it will start to behave erratically.

The other possibility is that the power supply will shut down altogether, and the machine will have to be switched off. It should also be mentioned that cooling and overloading the supply are related. As the computer's components get hotter they tend to draw more current, which tends to make them hotter, and so on.

You can calculate if there is enough power available, but you need to check the specs for your machine. The manual for the machine will tell you the current available in amps for each voltage supply, for each slot or for the entire set of slots. This may be something like 5 volts at 3 amps, 12 volts at 0.5 amps and − 12 volts at 200 milliamps.

Next, look at the specs for each board, which will tell you the maximum each will require at each voltage. Simply add the requirements, and pray that the current required is less than what is available.

If the current supplied is not enough for your boards, you may be able to get a heftier power supply for your computer.

It should be pointed out that there are many reasons other than power that a machine might stop running directly after the installation of a new board. On many boards, there are options which have to be set correctly (addresses and so on). In addition, there are cases where some of the boards are not compatible with each other, and you can use one or the other, but not both. Finally, there are the occasional instances where, although the power is sufficient and everything is set correctly, there is insufficient drive on some of the signals. That is to say, some signal output is connected to so many inputs on the various boards that it cannot operate properly.

Cooling

Cooling is another topic which is subject to paranoia. Some computer owners nose around inside their computers and say "gee, that feels warm," and start getting unnecessarily concerned about cooling. On the other hand, there is some basis for concern about keeping equipment reasonably well cooled. And, as mentioned above, if the available power is marginal, running too hot can put the system over the edge.

The first point to realize is that many computer components run hot, and will feel very hot to the touch. Even a small microprocessor might put out a few watts of heat, which it must dissipate into the air through a mere square inch or two of surface. Yet most components are specified to be capable of operating up to at least 70 degrees Celsius (about 160 degrees Farenheit). Next, while you are touching the chip, you are essentially insulating it, and it will seem to get hotter.

Many computers are designed to be cooled by convection only, and it is merely necessary to ensure that there is sufficient air circulation around the machine, and especially around any vents. Other computers have fans for increasing circulation inside the box, and of course, it is again necessary to keep these vents clear. In particular, try to avoid setting up your computer station so that the computer sits inside an enclosed desk compartment.

Is extra cooling necessary, as advertisers of fan kits would have us believe? No doubt you have heard at least one computer enthusiast talking about how somebody's computer ran much cooler and more *reliably* when a fan was added. They can't help but remind me of car enthusiasts who add spoilers and talk about the imagined gain.

As far as I am aware, only in rare instances has there been any evidence that after-market fans really did anything useful so far as a particular brand of machine is concerned, although the owners may have derived great satisfaction. These rare instances would include machines for which large after-market add-on boards appeared which were not originally allowed for in the design.

There definitely are cases where the addition of the fan covered up or confused the symptoms of some other intermittent problem. If your computer has an intermittent problem, then it is quite likely to be affected by heat. Such a problem might be a poor solder joint, or a bad connection inside a chip. The expansion due to heating disturbs such a bad connection, causing that intermittent failure. If you add a fan, the heating doesn't take place to the same extent, and the failure may not occur. In fact, technicians often locate intermittent components and connections by observing operation of the system while selectively spraying areas of the circuit board with *freeze spray*, which is available at electronics stores.

This causes an argument as to whether the fan did any good. In the sense that it allows the machine to be used more than without the fan, I suppose it was a benefit. On the other hand, the problem still exists, and may crop up at a later time.

The key to this argument would be to check with owners of other similar machines to see if they have experienced similar problems under similar circumstances.

Failures of Power Supply Connections

In older computer systems of perhaps five years or more, there is a quite common problem which is fairly easy to fix, and doing so can save much aggravation and expense.

As has been described above, the most critical power-supply voltage is the 5-volt line. In most computer systems, power is delivered to the main board as 5 volts, and must be 5 volts within 0.25 volt. This is in contrast to S-100 systems for example, where power is delivered to each board at about 8.5 volts and each board has its own regulator to provide local 5-volt power. There is probably also a +12-volt supply for RS-232 and disk-drive motors and a −12-volt supply, for RS-232. The total current requirement on the 5-volt line for the computer can be from 5 amps to 20 amps in a typical small computer.

Even the weakest IBM-PC 5-volt supply is capable of providing 7 amps, while heftier models can supply double that figure. LSI-11 computers draw somewhat more, while S-100 units draw even more. Macintoshes and Atari STs draw less owing to their smaller complement of chips.

Whatever the computer, the connectors carrying this main logic power are critically important. These are the connectors in the 5-volt line, and also in the ground line. Unfortunately, these connectors are also subject to high current, and in many cases are not completely adequate for the task.

Typically, the computer's internal power supply is equipped with a set of wires, perhaps 10 inches long, with a multipin nylon connector on the end. This nylon connector, shown in Figure 17-2, plugs onto pins on the main board. Sometimes the connector has all of the pins in a line, and in other cases the pins are arranged in a rectangle. These connectors are often refered to as *Molex connectors*,

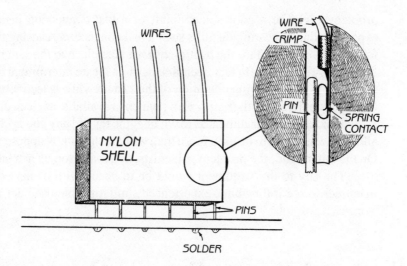

Figure 17-2   The infamous nylon power connectors are illustrated here, showing some of the major failure points.

although Molex is not the only company who makes them, and the bad things I have to say about them may not pertain to Molex's connectors in their correct applications. Some of the problems include the following:

1. The pins get wiggled and the solder holding them to the board may crack.

2. The pins and spring contacts may develop an unfriendly relationship.

3. The crimps which attach the wires to the spring contacts can become less than totally conductive.

In some machines, the power connection path may involve several sets of connectors: one on the power supply, another where the wires pass through the chassis at some point, and yet another onto the main board. Every point where such a connector exists provides several opportunities for a failure.

The first failure possibility is in the contacts themselves. After a few years, the contacts lose some of their springiness, so they don't push together so forcefully, and at the same time, some sort of corrosion takes place. The contacts turn a dark color, and their resistance at the contact point increases. If there is appreciable resistance in the contacts we now have a resistor which generates heat when current passes through. This heat accelerates the deterioration. It is not uncommon to see such connectors with actual burn marks on the nylon from the heat.

The other effect of the resistance is to reduce the voltage to the main board. If the main board draws 10 amps, then with a resistance of only 0.025 ohm, a very small amount, we have a voltage drop of 0.25 volt which will reduce a 5-volt supply to only 4.75 volts at the chips! This is our entire safety margin. Notice that in the best of situations we have two connectors to worry about, +5 volts and ground, so each must have a resistance of less than 0.012 ohm! Also remember that if any heat is generated at a bad contact, this may cause the voltage to worsen for some time after the computer is switched on at each session.

Because of the necessity to avoid even this very small resistance, many computers use several pins of the multipin connector for each of +5 volts and ground.

The second reason for concern about these connectors is that the pins are usually crimped onto the wires. This crimping is literally just a squeezing of the metal contact around the copper wire. It is subject to exactly the same problems as the contact points themselves!

If you are starting to experience seemingly unrelated intermittent failures, and you have access to a digital voltmeter, it would be worthwhile to check the 5-volt supply to the computer's circuitry. The easiest place to check for it is where it arrives at some ordinary logic chip. Look for any chip with a part number beginning with a 74, like SN7400X or 74LS645 or XX74HC374A. Measure across the corner pins as shown in Chapter 21 in Figure 21-8. *Be sure not to let your probes slip against adjoining pins or circuitry.*

If you get a reading below 4.85 volts or so, then be suspicious. Even though 4.85 volts is still OK, you may not be seeing the dips which occur under instantaneous peak-load conditions, nor what happens under adverse temperatures.

At any rate, it is also informative to measure the voltage across the power-supply wires directly from the power supply while it is still connected to the main board. The ground and +5-volt wires may be found either from the system documentation, or by guesswork. Also, rather than fuss with stripping back the insulation, you might try using some large sewing pins or needles plus clip leads to pierce the insulation and contact the power wires, so these won't require a repair later. This test should show a healthy 5.0 volts from the supply. The remainder is therefore being lost in the connector.

To satisfy your curiosity, you might also check exactly *which* connector is causing the loss by measuring *across* each connector pin. For example, measure the voltage from the actual power-supply ground wire *before* it enters the connector, across to the ground pin on a chip.

If you find a voltage across a connector that is more than 0.1 volt, this is cause for a repair. If power must travel through more than two connectors altogether, then a lesser voltage would be cause for action.

To fix the connector properly, replace the connector with a new one (both of the mating parts), and solder the pin contacts which attach to the wires. However, since it's probably Sunday and no replacement connectors are to be had, the second-best solution is this: simply cut off the existing connector and solder the wires straight to the main board! (When you cut off the connector, leave a short length of wire attached so you can see which color of wire attaches to what point. Beware of duplicate colors.)

This solution will reduce the removability of the main board of course, but will, at least, get you running again, and allow you to test the hypothesis that the connectors were at fault.

Screw-Contact Problems

A final example of power-connection failure can take place anywhere a power wire is screwed to a PC board. In a typical case, the wire is terminated in a circular lug or eyelet. This bolts into a large hole in the printed circuit board where the lug is held against a circular contact area around the hole.

This works for some years, but it is often doomed to failure. The board has probably been solder coated, including the area under the lug. The lug actually contacts the solder. Although the screw may have been fastened tightly, after some time the solder, which is very soft, gives a little and the assembly is now loose. This develops a high resistance, producing heat and so forth. To get back into action, simply tighten the bolt.

IDEAS THAT DIDN'T CATCH ON WITH THOSE STUBBORN MUSICIANS.

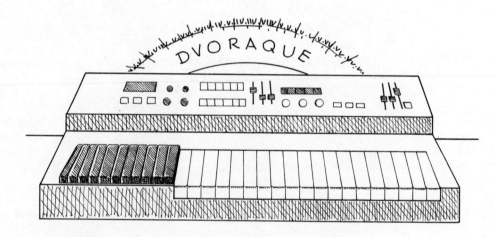

DVORAQUE

COMPUTER TECHNOLOGY BRINGS US TO THE
DVORAQUE SYNTHESIZER KEYBOARD, KEEPING ALL OF
THOSE NUISANCE BLACK KEYS OFF TO ONE SIDE WHERE
THEY STAY OUT OF TROUBLE.

18

Musical Instrument Digital Interface (MIDI)

Just as the microprocessor has brought us the personal computer, so it has also brought musicians more sophisticated electronic instruments. And in the early 1980's, a need was seen for some capability for electronic music systems to communicate.

Thus it was that several synthesizer manufacturers in the United States and Japan formed a committee to examine the matter. The result is Musical Instrument Digital Interface (MIDI). Actually, it would be more accurate to say that the result was a new era in cooperation and communication between synthesizer manufacturers, and MIDI is not only their first joint development, but the element which keeps them talking.

In 1984 through 1986, MIDI took off with rather astounding speed. Initially, I believe, it was envisioned as a scheme by which to attach a keyboard to a sound generator. However, it has evolved into a system for connecting multiple devices together including synthesizers, drum machines, reverb units, lighting, and, of course, a computer to record the session or control the whole show.

In effect, not only has MIDI brought computers to musicians, it has also helped to bring musical interests to computer enthusiasts.

In this chapter, I will endeavor to provide some background on MIDI, and some commentary on the job of hooking MIDI gear to computers, with a few suggestions for testing.

What Is MIDI?

MIDI is a convention for allowing pieces of music gear to communicate. In appearance, a MIDI hook-up simply looks like a cable between the two units. The cable uses 5-pin DIN connectors commonly refered to as *European Audio connec-*

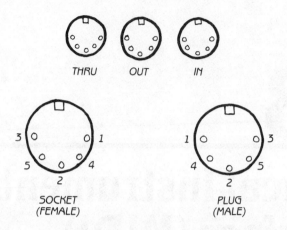

Figure 18-1   Typical back-panel of a MIDI-fied synthesizer.

tors, although MIDI signals are digital and not audio information. Actually, one cable only carries information one way, so two cables would be needed for a two-way conversation when this is necessary (Figure 18-1).

MIDI does not communicate sound as such. The information carried over MIDI is merely control information such as "Key A is pressed with velocity X," and so on. The MIDI standards specify not only the cable wiring, but also define a vocabulary of such messages.

The MIDI hardware sends serial data at 31.25k baud, or about 3000 bytes per second, in a manner very similar to RS-232. The actual electrical arrangement is somewhat different, with particular attention paid to avoiding possible electrical-noise problems. Most messages are one to three bytes long, so the maximum message rate is an average of 1500 messages per second.

Using MIDI

This section is intended for readers who may not have had any contact with MIDI at all. There are several typical applications where MIDI is used, and describing them will probably be quite sufficient for you to think up many more. Here are a few:

Keyboard To Sound Generator: This appears to be the archetypal application for MIDI. In this case, there is simply a single cable carrying information from a keyboard to a separate sound generator. The keyboard may contain no sound-generating capability of its own, or it might be a full-blown synthesizer itself. Similarly, the sound generator may be a full synthesizer with keyboard, or it might be just a box, perhaps a rack-mount unit, which only knows how to obey MIDI commands and make sounds. (Here we run into the terminology problem that "keyboard" may refer to just a keyboard, or to a complete keyboard-synthesizer. I will stick to the former.)

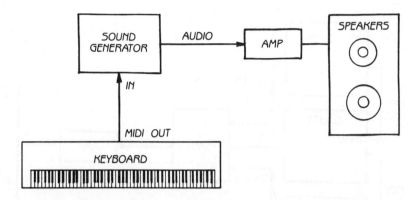

Figure 18-2   Simple MIDI configuration. Here a keyboard sends instructions to a sound-generator box.

One application for this set up would be where a performer has a keyboard with a particularly good feel, but prefers the sound or needs the capabilities of a different synthesizer. Or perhaps the performer wishes to use a strap-on, portable keyboard (Figure 18-2).

Keyboard To Many Sound Generators:

A MIDI system can be set up to cable a single keyboard to a chain of sound generators, using the MIDI *Thru feature*. A MIDI output can only talk to one input, so, in order to send a particular stream of messages to multiple instruments, most instruments provide a THRU jack which carries a copy of the "IN" signal.

The first thing that this permits is to have all of the sound generators play in unison for a "thicker" sound. However, MIDI includes a "channel" scheme whereby each message has an *address* number attached to it, and only listeners with that number respond to the message.

In this way the keyboard can send private messages to each unit. This means that the performer can very quickly switch between sound generators, have different generators responding to different parts of the keyboard, play harmonies and so on (Figure 18-3).

Non-Traditional Controllers:

A very up-and-coming field is the investigation of non-traditional controllers. The controller is the thing you play on, more technically referred to as a *gesture capturer*. Now, if you wish to build a strange-looking controller, it is merely necessary to build it right up to the MIDI interface, and then it can play sounds through a readily-available synthesizer.

Non-Keyboard Instruments:

MIDI is used on many non-keyboard instruments also. An example would be the connection between a set of electronic drum heads and the box which actually generates the drum sounds. In this case, the messages would select which sound is to be played depending upon which head was struck. The message would also affect the quality of the sound, that is, the loudness and timbre, depending perhaps on the force of the strike and even the location of the strike on the head.

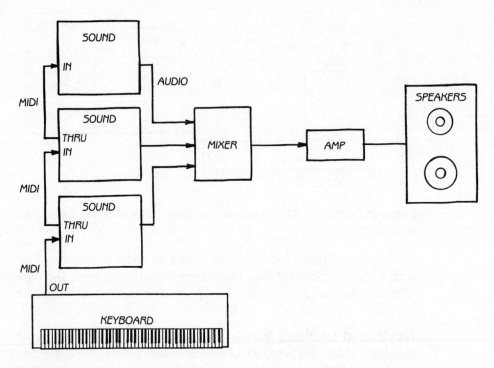

Figure 18-3   More expensive MIDI configuration. One keyboard plays multiple sound generator boxes.

Computer Involvement: MIDI interfaces are available for many computers, and some even come with a MIDI interface built-in.

When you bring a computer into the MIDI picture, it often becomes the focus of the system. Controllers send messages *into* the computer, and the computer is responsible for sending messages out to the sound generators. The computer runs software which records what the musician plays. Perhaps the musician will play multiple different parts on successive passes, much like using a multi-track tape-recorder. The software probably has a display mode, which shows what was played in traditional or other notation. In addition, there is usually an edit mode, which permits the user to manipulate the notes one by one.

The music can be replayed by the computer through the attached synthesizer(s). Notice that when creating a multi-part recording this way, the usual problems of tape noise from several layers of recording are avoided, since (optimally) everything is recorded only once from instrument to tape.

Naturally, with this aptitude for recording, the computer tends also to be involved with other aspects of the recording process, which potentially includes the necessity to synchronize to tape-sync signals, and to other non-MIDI timing sources, such as those used for film scores, and older drum machines. But that's another story.

Computer Control: MIDI's predefined messages are oriented most directly to the job of passing messages specifically related to the music, such as telling which note to turn on, how intensely, and so on. However, the MIDI hardware is simply a serial communications link, and is quite capable of carrying all sorts of other information, so long as talker and listener agree on the codes.

One application for this is to save and load *patch information* between computer and synthesizer. *Patch* is the term given to the collection of parameter settings which make the synthesizer voices sound a particular way. Many synthesizers are highly programmable in this respect, although normally this programming must be done through frustratingly awkward pushbuttons and inadequate displays on the synthesizer's front panel. Using a software package called a *patch editor/librarian*, the user can save, edit and keep organized a collection of patches from the relative convenience of the computer.

The messages which are sent to or from the synthesizer when relaying patch information are not part of the MIDI specification, but instead are unique to a particular manufacturer, or even a particular synthesizer.

Control via MIDI does not stop there, however. MIDI is used to control lighting gear, to control the settings on reverb, other units, mixers and other effects. The same computer software which can record musical information can also record the information for these units.

Sequencers: A sequencer may be a separate box, or it may be a built-in feature inside a synthesizer or drum machine. The sequencer's job is to remember a musical sequence or sequences and be able to regurgitate them. With luck, you can edit a sequence and change it around. This is similar to the job which the computer is capable of doing. However, sequencers are generally far more limited in their abilities, and lack extensive keyboards and displays. As such, they perform a subset of what a computer can do. This means that it can be awkward, difficult or impossible to achieve the same results with a sequencer as are possible with a computer. Sequencers came into being and are used simply because they can be built more cheaply than full computers.

There are occasions, however, when only a simple sequencing operation is needed, in which case it is easier to use a sequencer for the job than to contend with a whole computer.

How Much You Really Need To Know

At this stage in MIDI's short history, it seems that there is far less to worry about with MIDI than with RS-232 for example. Of course, that's not saying too much. MIDI seems quite easy to get going in a basic manner, but there are still some obscure problem areas to understand and deal with.

Delays and Signal Degradation

When multiple sound generators are to be controlled from a single source, the obvious way to implement this system is simply to take advantage of the MIDI Thru feature. The controller Out jack is cabled to sound generator A's In jack. Then sound generator A's Thru jack is connected to sound generator B's In jack, and so on.

After about four or five such connections, however, things may start to operate erratically. At each stage, the Thru signal is simply a retransmission of the In signal, with no effort to clean it up, so it contains some degradation. The exact width of the data pulses has not been retained. So, after four or five such retransmissions, the signal is rather poor.

To get around this problem, manufacturers have come out with boxes which split a single MIDI output into multiple cables. Such a box is simply reproducing the one MIDI signal several times. All of the reproductions are only one generation removed from the original. The multiple cables can then be connected to the multiple sound generators as required, with increased reliability.

Another trouble, although *not* actually related to this, is the problem of delays. Many musicians have noticed that certain combinations of controllers and sound generators seem very sluggish or inconsistent in responding to the movements of the fingers. These delays are in the order of 5 to 20 milliseconds or more. This has nothing to do with chaining many units together. Rather, it is the slowness of the software, either in transmitting the messages from the controller, which is unlikely, or in the receiver responding to the incoming messages. There is no way around this except to complain to the manufacturer, and software updates seem to be very frequent in this business.

Compatibilities

Whenever there is an opportunity to hook more than one item together, there have to be opportunities for incompatibility. Here are some of the possibilities:

Interface Boards: If your computer doesn't come with a built-in MIDI interface, then it is quite likely that you can obtain one. However, depending on the computer, there may be several MIDI interfaces to choose from, and you should choose carefully, since they do not necessarily look the same to the software. Your main interest will probably be in certain particular software packages, so it will be necessary to find out which interfaces will work with the packages of interest.

Incompatible Codes: MIDI, unfortunately, suffers from a somewhat-unique problem. On the one hand, an attempt has been made to specify a universal set of messages, and to encourage manufacturers to empower their machines to behave sensibly for each message. On the other hand, the subject of what exact functions we want synthesizers to perform continues to be an area for music research. Individual manufacturers continue to develop their products, and must often resort to special *Manufacturer's Exclusive* (non-standard) codes to implement the most advanced and exciting features. This, of course, raises the question of incompatibility. To an extent, incompatibility is to be expected as MIDI is really an attempt to shoot at a rapidly moving target.

Because of this, you may need to check quite carefully whether the particularly exciting features of one synthesizer are actually supported by the combination of computer hardware and software you propose to use.

Printers: Many music software packages have the capability to print scores or other graphic information. As usual, this means ensuring that the software and printer speak the same language, specifically with respect to the codes the printer understands in order to print graphics.

Testing

There may be occasions when you will need to test for the presence of a MIDI signal. You have just obtained your new MIDI synthesizer, your new MIDI interface card, your new MIDI software. Then you saw how expensive the official MIDI cables were, so you got some audio DIN cables. Now, when you plug everything together, it doesn't work. Maybe there is some option you have forgotten to select, or a switch left unflipped, or some cables which are wired wrongly.

At this point, it would be nice to know whether the computer's not talking, or the synthesizer is not listening. Here are a few strategies:

- If another synthesizer just happens to be lying around, obviously you could connect one synthesizer to the other, to see what happens. If not, you might at least see if the one synthesizer can talk to itself. Many synthesizers can be put into a mode (from the front panel) where the keyboard *only* sends out MIDI signals, and the sound generator *only* listens to incoming MIDI signals.

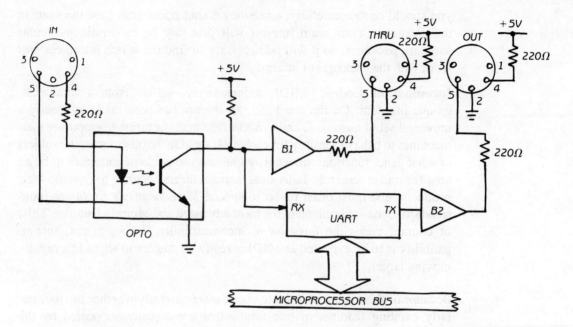

Figure 18-4   Schematic diagram of a typical MIDI interface inside a synthesizer.

In this mode, keying the synthesizer makes no sound, but you can now connect a cable from Out to In, and the synthesizer should play.

- If these strategies are unsatisfactory for your problem, then perhaps we can use some sort of signal monitors, as we did for RS-232 . . .

How the MIDI Interface Looks

Figure 18-4 is the schematic of what goes on behind the three MIDI connectors on a typical synthesizer. The In connector is attached to an *optoisolator*, which is a device which passes a digital signal, but does so with *no* electrical connection between input and output. The input to the optoisolator is an LED, the output is a photo sensitive transistor, and these two elements are put together in small IC package.

This feature is highly desirable in electronic instruments. Typically, quite a number of pieces of gear will ultimately be connected when you count instruments, mixers, amps and so on. Ideally, there will only be one signal-ground connection to each one. If there is more than one ground connection, a hum often results. Thus, the elimination of a direct electrical connection to the MIDI-receiver eliminates a possible source of hum problems.

At any rate, the optoisolator sends the received digital signal to a *UART*, which is a serial data receiving and transmitting chip. The UART handles communication for the synthesizer's microprocessor.

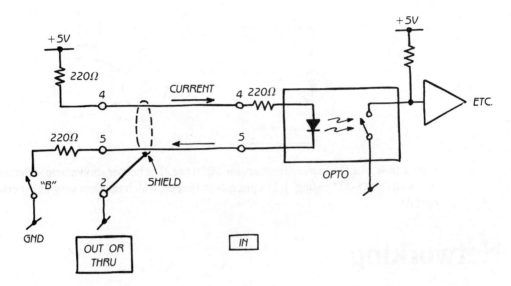

Figure 18-5   Here is a simplified picture of a MIDI output connected to a MIDI input.

At the same time, the optoisolator output is buffered (strengthened) and retransmitted out of the Thru connector.

When the microprocessor wants to send out some MIDI data, this is done using the UART also. The output serial data is buffered and fed to the Out connector.

When an output, (Out or Thru) is attached to an input (In), it looks like Figure 18-5. In this diagram, the output buffer has been replaced by a switch (B) to illustrate the essentials of how this interface works. In fact, it is a variety of current loop interface, in that it depends *not* on specific voltages, but on specific currents. The *shield* is the outer braid or foil conductor which is wrapped around the outside of the signal conductors. It prevents the MIDI signals from broadcasting and causing interference to other equipment. The shield is grounded *only* at the Out or Thru end of the cable.

Knowing how the interface looks, we now have the opportunity to attempt to apply our trusty beeper or LED testers, shown in Figure 18-6, which has been recycled from RS-232 uses.

The LED may indeed be attached to an Out or Thru signal, just as though it was the LED of the receiving optoisolator (Plus to Pin 4, Minus to Pin 5). This will definitely give an indication if the LED is the only thing plugged in (ie: no In attached). The indication on the LED tester, however, is quite dim owing to the high baud rate of the out data.

If the LED is attached while an In is also attached, it will tend to draw most of the current, and may disable the In.

The beeper is somewhat more useful. It can be attached whether or not an In is hooked up. When data is transmitted, the beeper will click like a cricket.

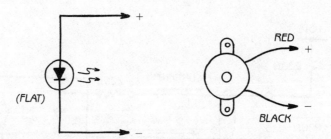

Figure 18-6   LED and Beeper testers for MIDI use. The beeper shown here is the same as that used for RS-232 testing. It is a piezo-type beeper, which requires very little current to operate.

Networking

As a last comment on MIDI, there is some talk about implementing a network with MIDI, especially in connection with the Atari 520ST. As it stands, MIDI would be far too slow for a reasonable network, and the speed is not arbitrarily restricted—it is slow because of the optoisolator in conjunction with the cable. Consequently, either MIDI-style networking is just talk, or it involves some sort of electrical interface which is more than mere MIDI. Specs for such a network are presently unavailable, so we'll have to wait and see.

DISK DRIVE INSIDE JOKE #375

19

Floppy Disk Drives

There are a number of reasons why it is worthwhile to understand a little about floppy disk drives and their connection:

- Installation of new or additional drives (Setting their options correctly).
- Pursuit of disk compatibility between different machines.
- Diagnosis of problems relating to drives.

Basic Operation

The best first step in understanding how a disk drive operates is to actually watch one in operation. Figure 19-1 shows the important parts of a typical disk drive.

The drive has the ability to record concentric circular *tracks* of information on one or both sides of the diskette, rather like a cross between a phonograph and a tape recorder, although the tracks are circular and not spiral. The drive's entire operation revolves around that purpose.

The circular plastic diskette is grasped by a cone shaped clamp and hub which also centers the disk as the drive door is closed. The main drive motor spins the disk inside its jacket at the very precise speed of 300 rpm for 5.25-inch drives.

The record/playback head is referred to as a *read/write head* in a disk drive. It is mounted on a carriage capable of moving in and out on slides along a radius. Because the tracks are at discrete locations, this movement is conveniently driven by a type of motor called a *stepper*. Unlike the familiar motors in blenders, fans and electric drills, a stepper motor is intended to run very slowly and precisely. In fact, it turns in steps of typically 200 or so exact steps per turn. Rotating the motor consists of pulsing it through one or more steps with the help of some controlling electronics. In a disk drive, the stepper motor drives the head in such a way that one step of the motor causes a head motion of one track.

If you are interested in stepper motors, you could do worse than to play with the stepper and controller from an old 5.25-inch drive!

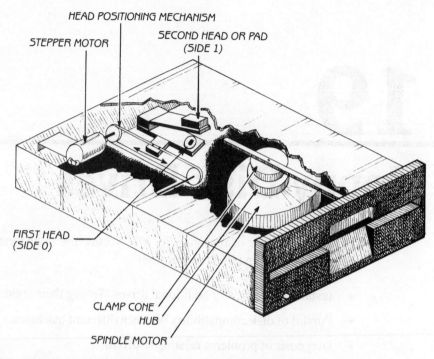

HEAD POSITIONING MECHANISM

STEPPER MOTOR

SECOND HEAD OR PAD
(SIDE 1)

FIRST HEAD
(SIDE 0)

CLAMP CONE
HUB
SPINDLE MOTOR

Figure 19-1   This is a typical disk drive and its most important parts.

On a 5.25-inch drive, 40 tracks per side are most often used with 48 tracks per inch measured along a radius; 80 is an alternative with 96 tracks per inch. Eight-inch drives use 77 tracks per side, while 3.5-inch drives use around 70 or 80 tracks at 135 tracks per inch, depending on the model.

A new diskette generally starts life unrecorded. *Formatting* or *initializing* a diskette consists of having the disk drive write some information at *every* track location. There are no physical tracks on the disk, just circles which have been recorded upon. The formatting operation writes markers for each track and section of track. The sections of track are called sectors. When real data (text, numbers, etc.) is written to the disk, the operating system will want to put it on specific sectors on specific tracks, and will check these markers to locate the proper place.

As you can see, it is critically important that the head-positioning system be very accurate, and agree very closely between drives.

If the drive is single sided, then there is just one head, and the other side of the diskette is held snuggly by a small soft pad. On a double sided drive the diskette is squeezed lightly between two heads.

Many drives stop at this point but others add a few embellishments. One common feature is to provide a *head-load* mechanism. In an economy drive, the head or heads are allowed to press ("load") against the disk surface as soon as the door is closed. In the luxury models, an extra solenoid operates a mechanism which normally holds back the head and only allows it to spring into operating position when needed.

Another feature, limited chiefly to 8-inch and 3.5-inch drives, is the ability to eject the diskette automatically, or to lock the door. This permits the software to control when the diskette may be removed, which ensures that it has been fully updated.

How the Computer Operates the Disk Drive

The operation of the disk system can be viewed as consisting of a number of layers. On the top is you, the user, who knows your file by name. At your command, or the command of your word-processor, is the operating system, which knows where on the disk your file resides. Actually, this information is stored in the directory area of the disk, but it is the operating system which knows how to interpret this in terms of specific tracks and sectors.

At the command of the operating system will be some lower-level routines which read or write to specific tracks. These communicate with a special-purpose disk-controller chip which actually operates the wires connected to the disk-drive unit itself. In addition, if data is being sent to or received from the drive, then the disk-controller chip functions as the intermediary. As such, it is responsible for converting the data from its parallel form on the computer's internal bus, to a serial stream of bits going to the drive where it is recorded one bit at a time on the selected track. The reverse process occurs for reading the disk.

In addition, the serial stream of actual data is sandwiched between other codes which are put on each sector of the track to make it possible to find the data later, and to check it for errors. This function is also handled automatically by the disk controller chip.

A look at the signals on the disk drive cable clearly show the kind of communication which is entailed. The following discussion relates to standard 8-inch, 5.25-inch and 3.5-inch drives, which are intended for use with standard disk-controller chips. These are the kind of drives used in most CP/M and MSDOS/PC systems, and in many others, such as the Atari ST. Non-standard drives are used in Apple products, but the basic principles of operation are similar.

All of the signals are digital, and, in most designs these signals are supplied to the drives on a single common ribbon cable. The signals follow the TTL voltage-level conventions. Actually, some of the signals are *open collector* signals as shown in Figure 19-2.

In this case, the output can only pull low or do nothing, while the input must have a pull-up resistor to provide a high signal when the output is doing nothing. For a disk-drive cable, this resistor is 150 ohms.

The fact that an open collector output can "do nothing" allows multiple outputs to connect to one signal line, as in the case of the outputs from multiple drives sending signals to the controller. Of course, it is necessary to ensure that only one drive attempts to send at a time.

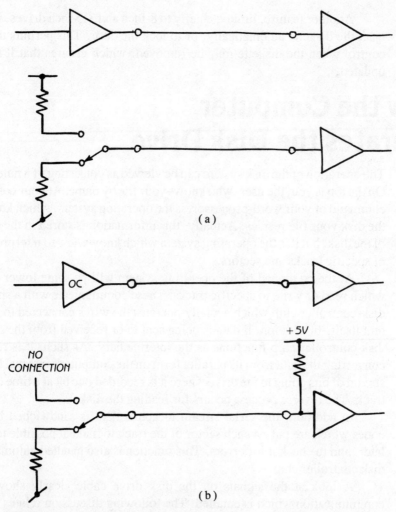

Figure 19-2   An ordinary TTL-style output has the ability to pull up as well as pull down. Not so with an open-collector output as shown in (b).

All signals are active in the low state. For example, the drive-select signals do nothing in the high state, but select the appropriate drive in the low state. The following is a representative list of the signals:

Drive Select Lines (From controller to drive(s)): There are usually 2 to 4 lines designated as drive-selects lines. These signals select which of up to four drives is the active one. In systems with multiple floppy drives, they are generally all connected to the same ribbon cable, and all are listening to the same signals from the controller. The drive-select lines determine which drive will obey the commands of the other signals.

In addition, some of the signals are sent *from* the drives to the controller. Since all drives share the same wires for sending signals to the controller, the drive select lines pick which drive will speak, and the remainder will wait for their turn to speak.

Motor On Line: This line tells the drives to turn on their disk-spinning motors.

Head Load Line (From controller): In some computer systems, the head is always pressed against the diskette surface or (*loaded*) when the door is closed. In other systems, these actions occur only in response to selection of the drive. In yet other systems, the head is loaded when the Motor On signal is active.

Side Select Line (From controller): The side of the active drive which will be read from or written to is selected by this signal.

Direction and Step Lines (From controller): These two lines control the movement of the read/write head, and consequently the selection of track. A pulse on the Step line causes the head of the selected drive to move one track in or out, as determined by the Direction line.

Track Zero Line (From selected drive): This signal indicates that the head on the selected drive is positioned at Track 0, the outermost track. This signal is used by software to *home* the head, which brings the head to a known position (for example, after powering up the computer). After homing, software can simply count how many tracks in and out the head has been moved in order to reach the desired track.

Actually, this is not the only way that software knows where the head is. In most disk formats, the track number is encoded into the *sector header* which precedes each sector of information on each track. However, neither method of determining track number is regarded as sufficient, and, if they don't agree, then an error may have occurred.

Index Line (From selected drive): If you inspect a diskette, you will see that there is a small hole in the plastic. When the disk spins, that hole is detected by a light beam arrangement in the disk drive. The pulse of light generates an electrical pulse which is sent to the controller. This allows the controller to know the position of the diskette. The controller uses this to format diskettes consistently, with the idea that the positioning of sectors on successive tracks can be optimized for speed of access when considering the time taken for moving the head from track to track.

Write Protect Line (From selected drive): Most drives permit you to designate a diskette as *write protected* or illegal to write upon. On 8-inch disks, this entails *removing* a sticker covering a notch. On 5.25-inch diskettes, write protection requires *attaching* a sticker over a notch. On 3.5-inch diskettes, a plastic slider is positioned for write protect or write enable. This is detected by the drive and signalled to the controller.

Write Enable Line (From controller, also called Write Gate): This signal tells the drive whether it should be reading the diskette or writing to it. It is used in conjunction with Write Data and Read Data Signals.

Write Data (From controller): Serial data from the controller is fed along this wire for recording onto the diskette. The drive processes this signal very little, simply converting it to the appropriate voltage and current to feed into the read/write head. The data rate on a 5.25-inch, double-density system (such as the PC) is 250k bits per second (including the extra codes added by the controller). On a single density system, the rate is 125k bits per second. The controller takes on the heavy responsibility for the exact timing of the recording process.

Read Data (From selected drive): When the drive is commanded to read (its normal state) the magnetic signals picked up by the read/write head are amplified into logic-level signals and sent to the controller. The controller operates in conjunction with some fancy electronics called a *data separator* to make sense of this signal and recover the data.

The recovered data is passed byte by byte to the computer's main processor which stashes it in memory. (Some computers use a separate chip to handle this transfer so that the main CPU is not tied up. This method is called *Direct Memory Access*, or DMA.) As the data comes in the controller chip checks to make sure that the correct sector was retreived, and that there were no errors.

Power: As yet, I have covered only the signals on the ribbon cable. Power to the drive is supplied by a separate cable, and differs between the different sizes of drives. The 5.25-inch drives require ground, +5 volts for the logic chips and +12 volts for the motors.

Drive Options

If you ever decide to add or replace a floppy drive, you will need to know how to set it up. Eight-inch drives cannot be covered here because their jumpering is complicated and peculiar to each brand. A technical manual and a great deal of patience are generally needed for each type. The 3.5-inch drives are, at present, used chiefly on systems where your hand is held so well that you need do nothing to get the job right.

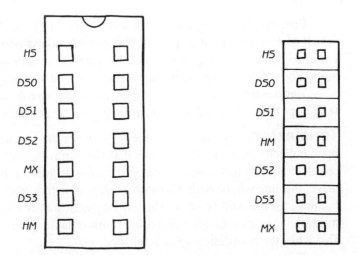

Figure 19-3   The option selection on most 5.25-inch drives is done with jumpers which either plug into an IC socket or onto a dual-row header that is, two rows of pins.

That leaves us with 5.25 inch systems, mainly CP/M and PC/MSDOS types. Inspecting the drive's electronics board, you will notice an arrangement of jumpers, either a double row of vertical pins with shorting blocks called *Bergs*, or an IC socket with a jumper plug whose legs can be removed from holes, or whose straps can be broken. There will also be another IC socket, hopefully labelled for a terminator. (See Figure 19-3).

Jumpers: The easy ones to take care of are the *drive select jumpers*, which determine which number this drive thinks it is. These are labeled DS0 to DS3. Install one jumper according to whether this drive will be 0, 1, 2, or 3 (correspond-ing to A, B, C, or D on most systems).

Oops! There's a twist on some PC systems, literally! Inside some real IBM PCs, a few conductors of the disk-drive ribbon cable perform a peculiar twist between Drive 0 and Drive 1. The object of this twist is to connect the two drive-select signals from the controller to the same pin on each of the two drive connectors! This is done so that both drives in this kind of PC can be jumpered as drive 0 at the factory.

Next we have jumpers labeled *HS* and *HM*. HS stands for *Head Solenoid*, and installing this jumper causes the head to load when the drive is selected. HM stands for *Head/Motor*, and causes the head to load when the Motor On signal is active. Either choice will work in principle. Notice that, in a multi-drive system, there is still just one Motor On signal, which turns on *all* the motors. Having all the heads load also with HM installed makes for speedier file copies between disks, as there will be no head load delay each time the drive selection changes. However, it would be best to observe what is used on the previously installed drive(s), and do the same. Note that you may *not* select both HS and HM.

Finally, there is a jumper labelled MX or *MUX*. This stands for multiplex, which of course is a lot of plexes. Since confusion is perplex, this means many confusions. Seriously, do not install this jumper. Installing it causes that drive to always be active, which means that it had better be the only drive in the system.

Various drives have other jumpers but these are non-standard, and one can at least hope that they were set to something sensible at the factory.

Terminator: As mentioned above, some of the signals on the drive cable are open collector signals. This means that the controller only has the capability to either do nothing to this wire, or to pull it firmly to ground. It is expected that, at the drive, this line will be pulled up with a resistor, so that when the controller is doing nothing, the line will be high. This arrangement was devised to make the communication between controller and drive more reliable, given the components available when the convention was established.

The problem is that we only need *one* pull-up resistor for each signal, and we might have up to four drives on the cable! For this reason, all of the lines which require a resistor are brought to an IC socket, where you can plug in a resistor pack. A resistor pack looks like an IC but, of course, it is full of resistors. This is the *terminator*. As with ICs, Pin 1 of the resistor pack is marked with a 1, a dot or a notch, and should be oriented to agree with a similar marking on the socket, and to be in the same orientation as ICs on the same board.

So, it is necessary to ensure that there is one and only one terminator installed between all the drives, and it should preferably be in the drive which is at the furthest point on the ribbon cable from the contoller.

Finally, when installing the new drive, it is necessary to determine which way the ribbon-cable card-edge connector fits onto the PC-board tongue. Some are keyed, but most will fit both ways. The fingers of the connector tongue are numbered 1 to 34, with odd numbers on one side, and even numbers on the other. This corresponds to consecutively counting the wires in the ribbon cable, with Wire 1 being next to the stripe on plain cable. So, look for some indication of Finger 1 or 2, and then attach the connector with the stripe at that side. Fortunately, if you *do* manage to get the connector on backwards, no permanent damage should result. Also, the drive will be constantly selected, yet otherwise will not work.

Disk Formats and Compatibility Among Systems

In many systems the disk drives are governed by a standard disk controller. This means that the format of the data on the disk is fairly well constrained. Consequently, it is theoretically possible to read and write diskettes from one system on another.

However, it should be remembered that there are a number of other obstacles to this process. Even if one machine can read sectors of data from the disk of another machine, it is still necessary to write extensive software for that machine to be able to find the location of the foreign directory, and to understand what it means. Even if this hurdle is conquered, there is still the likelihood that the application program which will work on the transfered file may not understand its contents!

A case which *will* work is the transfer of a WordStar file from Kaypro II to IBM PC. Either machine has a utility available for reading and writing foreign format disks and successfully dealing with the foreign directory. Thus, it is a simple matter to transfer the file to a diskette usable on the destination system. Then, because both CP/M and MSDOS versions of WordStar use the same special codes *inside* the text file, it is immediately usable on the destination system.

Another example is the transfer of a Lotus 1-2-3 data file from PC to Atari ST, for use in an ST spreadsheet. Although the diskette sizes are different, both machines use standard disk controller chips. So, either machine can be equipped with the other size drive and can be made to understand the foreign format. Commercial products for this purpose are available. This being so easy, writers of ST spreadsheets consider it worthwhile to be able to understand 1-2-3 type files, perhaps even without any file rearrangement.

One example which illustrates a problem is the transfer of a Microsoft Word text file from PC to Macintosh. The first problem is that the Mac does *not* use a standard controller chip. Instead, it uses a completely unique format, including disk drives which run at different speeds for different tracks, slowing down toward the inside for more constant bits-per-inch density. The Mac cannot hook up to a 5.25-inch drive, and a PC with a simple 3.5-inch drive is incapable of generating the disk format of the Mac.

Thus the transfer to and from the Mac must be done through a serial RS-232 communications link, with file transfer software at each end. Even having transfered the file, it turns out that MacWord stores different information in its text files than does PC Word, and one can't understand the other's files. Thankfully, Microsoft now provides a utility program to make this conversion. However, you can readily see the problem if you try to transfer, for example, a WordStar file to MacWrite.

Summary: If dissimilar systems both use standard disk controllers, then there is a good possibility that hardware and software is available to copy files from disk to disk, even if that means buying another size of drive for one machine. If one of the machines uses a non-standard disk-control arrangement, then the transfer must be done by communications link.

Whichever the case, simply transfering the files is not necessarily sufficient. Unless the information is simple text (lines of text with a carriage return/line feed at the end of every line), it is highly likely that the destination software will not be able to understand all of the information in the file. In that case, be careful to check into software whose specific purpose is to convert a file from the source software into something understandable by the destination software.

Disk Problems

There are many problems which can afflict your disk drives, some of which you can sort out yourself at minimum expense. I will restrict my comments to 5.25-inch drives here, because these are currently in the majority. The 3.5-inch drives will no doubt catch up, but it is not yet clear how much trouble they will provide, nor how standard they will be between systems. 8 inch drives, on the other hand, are on the way out, and beyond cleaning, they require a little more technical information to work on and to replace or repair.

This section is intended to guide you in becoming more informed about disk drive problems, which, at worst, will allow you to describe the problem better to a repair person. Also, you are allowed to use your own head and think of other tests, too.

I suppose I should recommend cleaning the drive first, before doing anything else. You can use a disk-drive cleaner diskette, although competing companies claim that each others' products do more harm than good. Instead of buying a commercial product, you can use a cotton swab with some alcohol to *gently* clean the heads. Some disassembly of your computer may be required to get to the drive, but do *not* disassemble the drive unit itself! Frankly, I don't recall a problem that was ever solved by cleaning the heads, except that it eliminated the possibility that dirt might be a problem. Still, you never know. And, while you're at it, if it's a single-sided drive, check that the head-load pad hasn't fallen off.

So on to "The Fix" for most real problems. In most cases, a problem can be solved with "the swap." The Swap is to just buy a replacement drive and install it, rather than fuss about fixing the old one. With drive prices in the $70-range, it's not worth the worry. Be sure to get a replacement that is suited for your system. You'll need to specify single- or double-sided drives, and 48 tracks per inch or 96 tracks per inch. The most common is double sided 48 tracks per inch, which is what the PC and many other machines use. You may also care about physical size (full-, half- or third-height) and the aesthetics of the style of door. Also, don't forget, Apple drives are different.

The reason I mention "The Fix" before getting to "The Problems" is to remind you not to waste too much effort on "The Diagnosis."

When a problem occurs with a disk drive, it generally shows up first as trouble reading from or writing to a disk. So, the first thing to do is to eliminate the possibility that the problem is specific to a particular diskette. Perform extensive tests on a different diskette, with a completely different set of software. Bear in mind that some problems will not show up until the disk is fairly full, which can be arranged by some judicious copying activity. But be careful that the problem is not *just* that the disk is full!

Next, check to see if the problem might not be in one drive attempting to read or write a disk formatted in the other drive, and vice versa. If a drive is quite happy with its own disks, but can't work with disks from another drive, then it's time for "The Swap." While you are waiting for the new drive, you might check which drive it is which should be replaced, by checking which disks from other machines will work.

If the problem seems to be with the drive that you use to boot your system, then you will need to interchange drives so that you can boot at all. This will entail attending to the jumpers and terminator mentioned earlier.

There are also some problems which might be due to a supposedly inactive drive butting in and screwing up communication to another drive. If this seems possible, disconnect each drive in turn to test this out.

I have one last trick for you concerning 5.25-inch drives: have you ever had to use someone else's computer and felt stupid when you had to ask which way to stick the diskette into the drives because the doors were unfamiliar? Well, there's an easy way to determine this. The door mechanism is *always* involved in clamping the diskette, and *the diskette is always clamped on the label side*. Thus, the label should face the side of the drive slot with the door, moveable tab, lever, or whatever mechanical gadget looks like it would do some clamping on the inside.

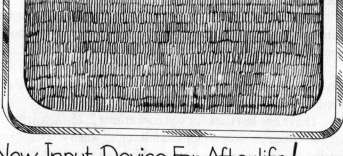

COMPUTER NEWS

Sunny Today
Dark Tonight!

20

Miscellaneous Connections

In this chapter, I have collected together explanations and commentary on a variety of items which hook up to, or inside, your computer. These provide some background on the operation of the various items, and some information on the choice of options and solution of problems.

Having gathered the information, it seemed that most of it relates to input devices, and consequently, this chapter is largely a survey of methods to input information into your computer.

Keyboards

So far as the average user is concerned, keyboards are not a matter of much worry. With some computer systems, the keyboard is solidly attached to the main computer box, and is not changeable. With other systems, the keyboard is a separate item, and a selection of different models are available. Then, there are systems where the keyboard is separate, but still there is no choice of alternates.

If there *is* a choice of keyboards, you merely select among keyboards suitable for your system, and that's that. The selection of keyboard depends on a number of characteristics of the keyboard, which include:

Key Layout: Placement of keys can make a very big difference in how well you get along with a particular keyboard. IBM is infamous for their PC keyboard which placed the little-used backslash key between the Z and the Shift keys. This is an absolute nightmare for anyone who expects the shift next to the Z. Then there are considerations such as size of important keys like RETURN, and whether there is a separate numeric pad and cursor-key set.

Key Feel: Key feel is a rather complex subject. On the surface, it would seem merely to entail the firmness of the key, and possibly whether the key snaps as it is depressed. This is called *tactile feedback*. The key may or may not generate an audible click.

However, there are other characteristics, such as the depth of travel which the key permits. Also important is how far the key must be depressed before the keystroke is detected.

Key Tops: An inspection of a variety of keyboards shows that there are a couple of contouring considerations. One contour is that of the individual key tops. On some keyboards the key tops are dished in two dimensions (i.e., a drop of water would be cradled), while in an increasing number of keyboards, the keys are dished only from side to side (a drop of water would dribble out toward the user).

The other contour is that of the overall keyboard. In a heavily contoured keyboard, the keys are arranged as in a steeply-tiered theatre, which perhaps brings the numeric keys or function keys into better accessibility.

Summary: It is often said and written that choice of keyboard is a matter of personal taste. To be sure, taste is involved, but my opinion is that this is really over-used as an excuse to sell bad keyboards, and to deny that research into the matter would demonstrate principles for good design.

At any rate, if you have a choice, I urge you not to be satisfied with an inferior keyboard. You may easily type millions of strokes on it, so you should be happy with it. Do *not* be lulled into thinking that you can become used to any arbitrary keyboard. A musician does not suppose that he or she will become used to an inferior instrument, so it stands to reason that if you work with a keyboard, you should allow yourself to be particular. Having studied the problem at some length, I hereby contribute my thoughts on the matter.

First, key layout is indeed important, and must be compared to the layout you are already familiar with, or others you must work with frequently. There is no doubt that key complement and layout could be improved tremendously, but you may be constrained by other keyboards that you must continue to use.

However, just because this is the most visible aspect of the keyboard does not mean that it is necessarily the most important. Possibly more crucial is how well the keyboard responds to your attempts to make correct keystrokes.

This may sound a little silly, but it's not. Consider in detail the movement of the finger as it performs a keystroke. In some cases, the finger may be already resting atop the necessary key, and merely pushes straight down. But in many other cases, the finger is off to one side, and must fly in like a plane coming in for landing. This is *especially* true for non-touch-typists, who move their hands away from the keys in order to be able to see the key legends!

Therefore, we would like the keyboard to be as helpful as possible in assuring a safe landing for that flying finger. This can be achieved in a number of ways. First, the keys should *not* respond over-sensitively to an accidental brush which might occur as the finger moves toward the correct key. For this, the keys should be somewhat firm, but, in addition, the key should require being depressed an appreciable distance before registering the hit.

As the finger arrives at the correct key, there is still a possibility that it might overshoot. This possibility is reduced if the finger tip is "caught" in the key-top. So, of course, this makes me suggest that the two-dimensionally dished tops are better than the one-dimensional dishes, which, in turn, are better than absolutely flat tops. And contouring of the overall keyboard can help in this process also.

Keyboard Interfaces

Most keyboards are simply an arrangement of so many switches. However, these are *not* each individually read by the main processor. In fact, in most cases there is special-purpose chip, perhaps a dedicated microprocessor, looking after the keyboard. Even that chip doesn't look at each of the keys individually. Instead, the key switches are wired up in a matrix arrangement, and are *scanned*. This story will be presented in more detail in the chapter on custom interfacing.

Having noted that there is a dedicated chip looking after the keyboard, this leads to an explanation of the way detached keyboards communicate with the main computer box. As you may have noticed, PC-type computers use a coiled cord with a circular five pin plug, while the Kaypro II and its descendants, and the Macintosh use small, modular-telephone-style connectors.

If you haven't guessed already, the keystroke information is communicated serially from the keyboard to the main box. Two wires in the cord supply power to the keyboard's microprocessor, and one or two wires are used for communication from the keyboard to the main box. At first, you could envision this serial communication to be just like RS-232, except that the voltages used are 0 volts and 5 volts, rather than plus or minus 12 volts.

However, in the PC for example, there is also a clock wire. If you read the section on RS-232, you may recall that a major function of the receiving communications chip, the UART, is to stay in step with the transmitter, so as to know which bit is which. In the PC's system, a clock signal is used to keep the receiving chip in step, which allows the use of a very inexpensive receiving chip.

In addition, the PC keyboard scheme includes a method by which to reset the keyboard's microprocessor to it's initial state, and also a method to disable the keyboard if the operating system has no more room in its key queue.

As a result of the particular functions implemented for each computer manufacturer's keyboard, there is little in the way of interchangeability of keyboards intended for different types of machine. Most PC and PC-clone keyboards are interchangeable between clones, but cannot be used on the Macintosh or

Kaypro II, or even on the PC-AT. So, unfortunately, if you find a keyboard for one kind of computer which you *really like*, you almost definitely will not be able to use it on another kind of computer.

Game Ports and Joysticks

From the point of view of merely selecting joysticks for purchase, the customer should have little difficulty in simply requesting a model suited for the particular brand of computer. However, there are a number of reasons why readers may be interested in a deeper understanding of what is entailed in a joystick.

For a typical computer, a joystick unit will typically consist of the joystick handle which can move in four directions (north, south, east and west, as it were) or between directions. In addition, there are usually one to three pushbuttons, one of which may be atop the stick. The computer will probably accomodate two or more such joysticks.

Despite external appearances, there are two quite-different designs of joystick with different capabilities. One design, which is used on the Atari and several other machines is what we might call the simple "switch" design (Figure 20-1). In this design, there are four switches inside the joystick. Moving the joystick in one of the four compass directions closes one of the switches. These switches are attached to input lines into the computer, by which software can read the direction. Similarly, the one to three buttons feed into inputs which software can read.

If the joystick is moved to a diagonal position, then two switches are closed, which again informs the software of the position. However, this system implies that there are only eight unique joystick directions, plus neutral.

Contrastingly, there is another design of joystick used with other computers (for example Apple IIs and PCs) which *can* sense intermediate positions (Figure 20-2). This design uses two potentiometers (variable resistors) which are operated by the movement of the joystick—one each for the X and Y axes. These are called *analog joysticks*. The computers which use analog joysticks have the electronics necessary to measure the resistance of each potentiometer.

The resistance of each potentiometer is measured by the computer's circuitry, and converted to a number between 0 and 255, with 127 being the mid position. Thus, there are actually a total of 256 multiplied by 256 different, unique positions for this kind of joystick. The software can determine a direction and a distance from neutral if those parameters are relevant to the task at hand.

As an example of the difference that these two designs make, imagine some software in which an object (perhaps a cursor, spaceship or drawing pen) is moved about the screen by the joystick. Let's suppose that the joystick action doesn't *directly* position the object, but merely causes the object to proceed in that direction, while neutral stops the movement. In the case of the switched joystick,

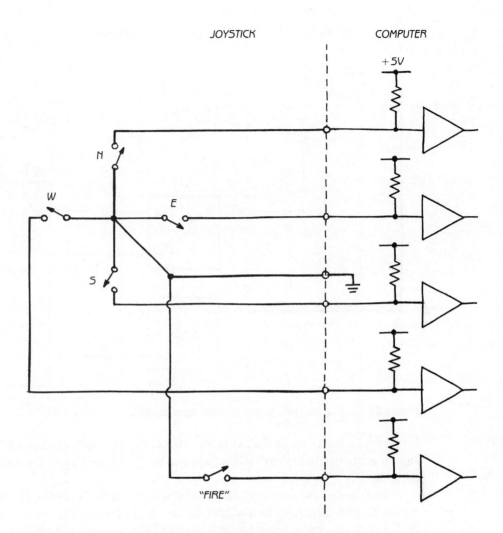

Figure 20-1 Diagram of a switch-type joystick.

the user can only tell the object which direction of 8 possible directions to move at a fixed speed. However, with the potentiometer stick, the user can select direction more precisely, and can control speed of movement also.

There is more to be said about joystick and switch inputs, but I have reserved this for Chapter 21, which covers Custom Interfacing.

Joysticks and Software

Usually, when switches are read into the computer, it is a simple matter of reading some input port or memory location corresponding to an input, and then figuring out what values of number indicate which switches are closed. In fact, on machines

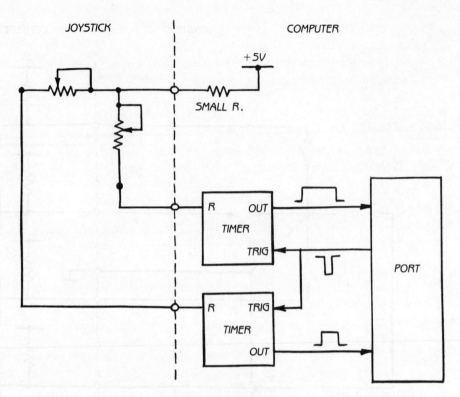

Figure 20-2   Diagram of a potentiometer-style joystick.

for which joysticks are available, there is usually a built-in routine which you can call, or a function built in to the language you are using, to tell you this information more directly.

Switches, then, are easy. But what about the potentiometer-type joysticks? Again, there is usually some available routine or function to tell you the numbers. But, it is still useful to know how the numbers are arrived at. As it turns out, the cheapest way for manufacturers to hook up analog joysticks is *not* to use an analog-to-digital converter. Instead, a timer chip is used (a 555 or similar chip for those familiar with timers). A timer chip is simply an IC which can perform very simple-minded timing functions. In this case, it is used in the mode where a short input pulse triggers the timer's output pulse. That output pulse length is determined by the value of a resistor which is attached.

In the joystick application, the two joystick potentiometers are attached to two timers. When the software needs to read the joysticks, it sends a pulse to trigger the timers. Then the software simply sits in a loop, counting and watching the timer-output pulses. When each pulse ends, the software remembers the count that had been reached, and this reflects the position of the joystick.

To be sure, this is a very cheap and workable way of handling joysticks. The only disadvantage is that all of this counting and waiting for the joystick timers might consume a couple of milliseconds. This could be very important if you would rather have your program doing something more useful!

Mouses

For a device with such a timid name, the mouse has certainly made bold strides into the computer world of late. As a consequence, we see a variety of mouse types, depending upon whether the mouse was designed to be part of the original computer product, or was added at a later date.

Actually, the variety in designs arises partly from different methods of detecting movement of the mouse, and partly from different methods of connecting the mouse to the computer.

The most common type of mouse has a motion detection scheme which consists of a ball which turns when the mouse is moved across a flat surface. Inside the mouse, this ball turns wheels which respond only to movement in the X or Y directions respectively. The wheels have an arrangement of spokes which interrupt and pulse a light beam apparatus when the mouse is moved. The light beam device can also detect the direction of movement. Actually this requires two beams and two signals for each axis (pictured in Figure 20-3).

For some machines, like the Mac and the Atari ST series, the pulsing light-beam signals (four in all) are treated by some electronics and made into TTL-style signals which are then simply fed into some inputs on the computer. In fact, on the ST, the mouse is handled by a connector which can alternatively handle a joystick instead. The four lines which handle the light-beam signals of a mouse also are the ones which handle the four direction switches of a switch-type joystick! However, different software would be required in each case. The buttons on a mouse likewise simply feed into TTL-type inputs on the computer.

Another variation of mouse motion-detection is that from Mouse Systems. In their design, there are no moving parts, but the mouse must be moved about on a special mouse pad which is provided. This pad has a fine grid of vertical and horizontal stripes of different colors. On the underside of the mouse are a pair of reflective sensors (LEDs and phototransistors), each sensitive to just one of the colors. In this way, the mouse-tronics can detect line-crossings, and, thus, knows about mouse movements.

The other major variation in mice comes from the use of an RS-232 interface for the mouse instead of a set of switch-type signals. The result is a more complicated mouse, but this is necessary on computer systems where mouse hook-up would otherwise be difficult, such as on the PC.

(a)

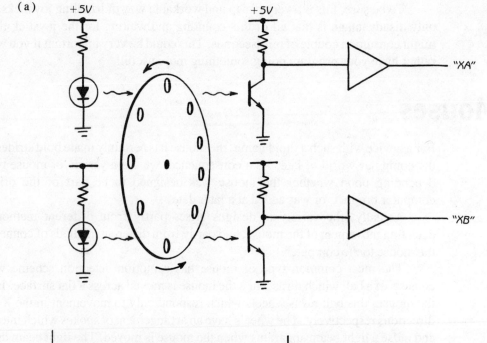

(b)

Figure 20-3   A diagram showing the mouse and how it operates.

Mouse Software

In computers where the mouse is an essential feature, operation of the mouse goes on behind the scenes. At the most superficial level, the user doesn't have to worry about the mouse on a Mac, or an ST or an Amiga, because the application software, that is, the word-processor, spread-sheet program etc., already assumes it's there and will use it.

However, it is interesting to note *how* it is used. In the Mac for example, the mouse has control over the cursor arrow by virtue of built-in, interrupt-driven mouse routines. What the application software is interested in is the location of the arrow, or, what it is positioned over. If the application software sees that you have pushed or clicked the mouse button, and the arrow is at a special location, over a menu heading, for example, *then* that software takes a special action.

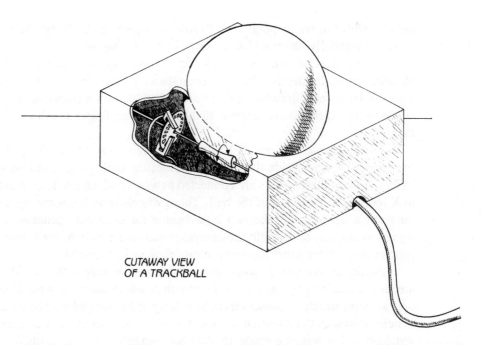

CUTAWAY VIEW
OF A TRACKBALL

Figure 20-4   The trackball mechanism is very similar in principle to that of a mouse. This drawing shows one of the rollers which picks up motion of one direction. The roller turns the spoked wheel, which interrupts the two light beams.

This contrasts drastically to the way the mouse is handled in a PC system. First of all, the PC never expected to be connecting with a mouse, so the mouse has to hook on to an RS-232 serial port. Then, a software routine or driver must be installed. This would be provided by the mouse manufacturer. The driver attends to data coming in from the mouse. The incoming data is translated into appropriate key codes and stuck into the keyboard queue. Sometimes movements of the mouse are made to look like the user was tapping frantically on the keyboard cursor keys!

This is done because the existing applications software knows what to do with keystrokes, but not with a mouse. It is a compromise which works, but it's not as smooth as the more up-to-date approach. In addition, different drivers must be installed which are appropriate for different applications packages, since not all software uses the cursor keys uniformly, and certainly the mouse buttons will need to look like different keys.

Trackball

The trackball shown in Figure 20-4, is another input device for positioning. In appearance, it looks like a pool ball held in a box with most of the northern hemisphere of the ball exposed. The ball is free to turn in its box, and the user rolls the ball with fingers or palm which typically moves a cursor on the computer's screen. Essentially, the trackball is an upside-down mouse.

Despite its relative unfamiliarity, the trackball can be surprisingly speedy and pleasant to use. It affords better precision than a mouse, and sits still on the desk. There is however a drawback: there are no buttons on a trackball because they would be very difficult to operate with the hand whose finger or palm is also rolling the ball.

The mechanics of a trackball are in principle very similar to those of a mouse. In a typical design, inside the trackball's case, the ball is supported on system of rollers. Two of these rollers are connected to wheels which rotate only in response to X motion or Y motion of the ball. These wheels have holes and spokes which interrupt a light beam. The two light beams for each axis generate TTL-style signals which can be fed into the computer just like a switch input (assuming, of course, that the computer has some appropriate switch inputs).

Again, the computer's software must know what to do with a trackball. There are, at present, no popular personal computers which integrate a trackball, so the only systems which do possess trackballs have had them added. The mouse-based systems deal with the trackball in the same way as they would a mouse, except that some provision must be made for lack of switches, such as using keys on the keyboard as substitutes. In a PC-type system, either the application software must know what to do with the trackball, or, as in the case of a mouse, a software driver needs to be used to convert trackball information into fake keystrokes.

Miscellaneous Pointing Devices

Man has yet to finish devising newer and better input devices for his computers. Here is a selection which varies in accuracy and convenience:

Touch Pads: Various designs of Touch Pads have appeared over the years. They vary in size from about 4-inches square to 12-inches square. Their basic mode of operation is to detect when a finger pushes (and in most cases it's a firm push) on the surface, and to report that location to the computer.

Some pads have sandwiches of resistive material, and detect the resistance from your finger depression to the edges of the pad. Other pads have sandwiches whose lower layer is a sheet of plastic with closely spaced "X" conductors, and an upper layer with closely spaced "Y" conductors. In between is a layer which normally holds the upper and lower layers apart, but which deforms to allow the two surfaces to contact if depressed by a finger. Electronics determines which X wires contacted which Y wires, and thereby determines your position.

The accuracy of touch pads is an important question. For starters, the accuracy can be no better than the size of your fingertip. However, a large pad with a good sensing mechanism could be as precise as a few percent of the overall length.

Touch pads are often used with printed overlays which designate certain areas as "buttons" for different functions. The software, of course, must know which areas do what. This sounds good except that there is little on the flat surface to guide the fingers to the buttons.

As drawing tools, touch pads are marginal because the drawing you are producing is on the screen, not on the pad. (The pad becomes more of a cursor-moving device than a drawing device.) On the other hand, an existing drawing on paper can be placed on top of the pad and traced fairly well.

Digitizer Pads: These are the "professional" touch pads in a sense. In appearance, digitizer pads look much like touch pads except that they employ a pointer device which looks like a mouse with a crosshair magnifying glass which is sometimes called a *puck*.

In a typical pad, the pad itself contains a grid of X and Y wires carrying special distinctive signals. The pointer contains an "antenna" which picks up these signals, and thereby reports its position to the main pad electronics. From there, the pad sends the information to the computer, often by RS-232.

Digitizers are often used for inputing drawings to computers, particularly existing drawings. Existing drawings or pictures can be placed on the pad, and the pointer on top of that. They are also useful for inputing the locations of details of interest on photographs and maps. Some digitizer pads permit an image (for example, slides or video) to be projected on the surface of the pad from the rear.

Touch Screens: In some ways the touch screen seems like the ideal device because it allows you to point directly at a particular location of an image on the screen. Touch screens have never caught on very well, and there seem to be two reasons. One is that since the pointing device is a finger, if is not very precise. For example, it is not precise enough to point unambiguously at a particular character on a screen full of text. A second problem (believe it or not) is that the touch screen requires moving the hand from the keyboard to the screen, which requires effort.

Again, various actual implementations have been tried. One design involves a tricky resistive membrane which covers the screen. The touch of a finger is sensed by the electronics which determines the position based on the resistance to the edges of the membrane.

Another design was used on the elegant, but not widely purchased, Hewlett Packard HP 150 Touch Screen computer. This design involved surrounding the screen with a "picture frame" which enclosed an X-Y matrix of light-beams, composed of LEDs on two sides and photodetectors along the other two sides. Touching the screen breaks some of the light beams, and the electronics determines the location of the finger. Again, this system could not pick out a single character from 80-column text, but it was useful for selection of menu items and the like.

Light Pens: These are another variety of pointing device used with the computer screen. In appearance, a light pen literally looks like a pen with a curly-cord connecting it to the computer. Several computers have light-pen connections, including the PC. Recently, a light pen was even introduced with no cord at all. Must work by magic or something!

Anyhow, the light pen is pointed at the computer screen, usually up close, probably touching the glass. A selection is made by pushing a button on the pen. Inside the pen is a photodetector which is looking at the screen. When the electron beam in the picture tube scans past the "eye" of the pen, this causes a pulse of brightness, which the pen translates to an electrical pulse and sends to the computer.

Since the computer itself is responsible for scanning the electron beam by virtue of the video signals it sends to the monitor, it knows where the beam is when it receives the pulse from the light pen, and can work out the position of the pen.

The system works, but there are some problems. First, the screen which is used must have a phosphor whose brightness decays fairly rapidly after the passage of the beam. Many of the more pleasant-to-view screens have a *long decay* phosphor coating, and do not provide the pen with a sharp pulse of light. Recall that our eyes do not see this pulsing in either type of monitor as the screen is redrawn every 60th of a second, which is faster than the retina can follow. However, on the slower phosphor monitors, you may see a smeary trailing effect as text scrolls by rapidly on the screen.

A second problem with the light pen is that it only works if you are pointing to an illuminated area of the screen. This means that the screen must be presented with a bright background (not customary on many machines), or the screen must be "flashed" when you hit the pen button. If the latter is done, this can result in an inaccurate positioning because many monitors do not maintain a consistent size and positioning of image with different brightnesses.

A final pen problem lies in the optics of the pen and the screen surface. It seems that it is quite difficult to design a pen which is consistent in the way it sees the screen. Thus, while holding the pen at a particular location on the glass, the location detected by the computer can be quite sensitive to minor angling of the pen away from perpendicular.

So, the light pen joins the list of pointing devices which are not very good at accuracy but can be used for picking menu choices. An indication of the popularity of the light pen can be gained from the fact that one particular PC clone sold thousands of copies before it was discovered that its light pen routine was totally useless.

Bar Code Readers

Many consumer products, particularly grocery store items, are labelled with a printed code consisting of a series of narrow stripes in a rectangle. This is called a *Bar Code*. There are wands available which can be passed over these codes to read them into the computer. (The wand contains an LED which shines on the code, and a photodetector which sees the light and dark stripes.)

There are several different code conventions, but all can be read with the same wands, provided the software knows what it is doing. By obtaining such a wand, you could obviously use a computer to keep track of inventory by using the existing bar codes on the products.

On the other hand, you may have an application for making up your own bar-code system. You can print up the bar-code labels on a dot-matrix printer, and read them with an appropriate wand. This might be useful in a chemical storeroom, for an electronic component inventory, to track equipment subassemblies as they are manufactured, to check out books or video tapes at a library, or a host of other applications.

Appliance Control

A visit to your local hardware or department store will probably bring you into contact with a system by which you can turn household appliances and lights on and off from your bedside or wherever location you choose (Figure 20-5). The objects of this system are convenience and security. This system has been most widely distributed by a company called BSR.

In the hardware-store model, the main controller consists of a box with a collection of pushbuttons which plugs into a wall socket. Then, each appliance or light to be controlled is plugged into a small *slave control module* which itself plugs into a wall socket near the appliance or light. Now the controller is able to communicate with each of the control modules via high-frequency signals it sends along the household electrical wiring.

The slave modules are available in a number of different models, including units which simply switch on and off, and others which operate as variable dimmers. Each module is addressable so that the main controller can talk to each slave independently.

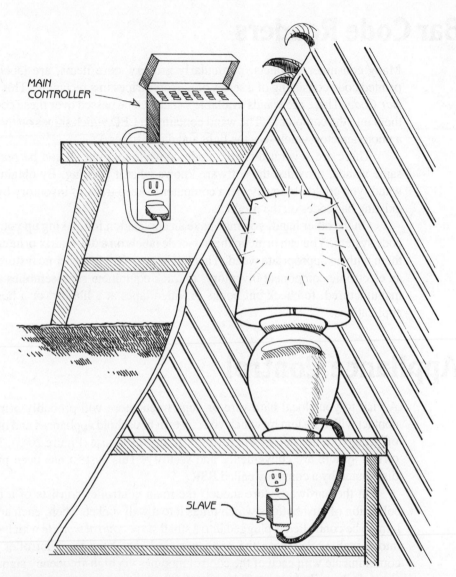

Figure 20-5   The principal components of an ordinary appliance remote-control system, which sends messages via the household wiring.

Naturally, it was not too long before it seemed like a good idea to make controllers which hook up to personal computers. These controllers can be programmed from the language of your choice. There are a number of such units available for different computer systems. These are periodically advertised in computer magazines.

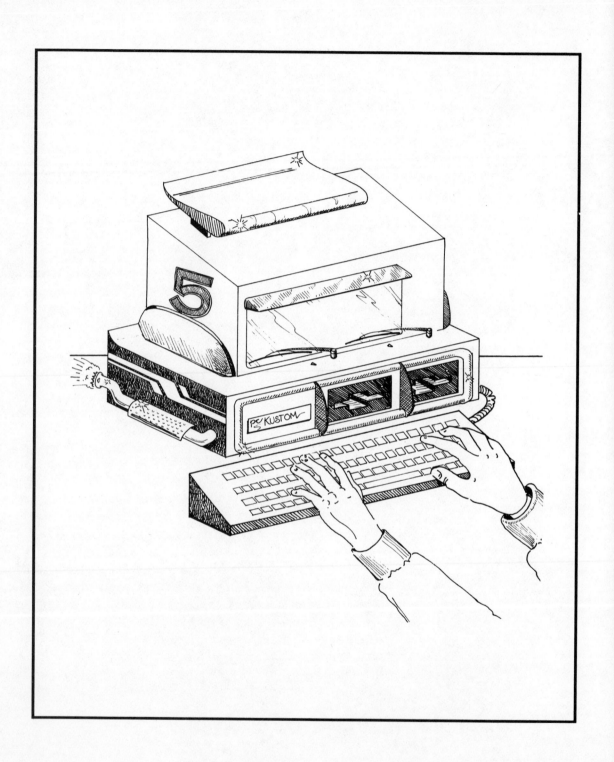

21

Custom Connections

One of the fascinating aspects of the personal computer is the potential it has for hooking on to devices of your own specification. Small computers can be used to control industrial processes, to control and collect data from experiments, to control appliances and security systems, along with various other applications.

But, even though these applications may be very useful, and certainly provide convenience, somehow their mention doesn't quite capture the feeling of creativity involved in custom-interfacing projects. I suspect that this is because, so far as the average computer user is concerned, all of these applications could have been fulfilled by some giant corporation somewhere, and then simply sold to the customer ready to go.

No, the feeling I am writing of is truly that of personal individual creativity which comes from doing something unique. Some people paint or sculpt, some are musicians, some create fantasy worlds as writers of books, plays or movies. Others derive immense satisfaction from creating a machine which does something neat. Indeed, artists and musicians themselves are using custom-interfaced computers to produce new works of art and music, some of these in which the viewer or listener is an active participant.

Think of the potential which the computer has for allowing the participant to experience the dynamics of an artist's statement, rather than merely viewing a static piece, or a moving one whose changes are preplanned and themselves unchanging.

If you have picked up this book, then you are probably the sort of person who is not satisfied merely to use what is provided to you off the shelf. There is a good probability that you have had a go at programming, indeed you might even be a professional in the software field. If that is the case, you have already done some creating on your own in the form of software. Perhaps you wrote a game, or just a convenient macro for your word-processor or spread-sheet. You are starting to say, "Hey, I can play in this game too, look what I can do."

But all of those software efforts, no matter how nifty, are still locked inside that box. You have to view them from the other side of the glass window, as it were. This chapter is an introduction to the world of hooking custom equipment on to a personal computer. It is not intended to be a complete treatise on the subject. It is intended to give you an overview so that you can decide whether you are interested, and will give you some idea of the terrain. I will show you some ways in which you can hook on to your computer as it stands, with little or no expense, and provide some idea of the more comprehensive and complicated approaches available for major projects.

As an Introduction to Electronics

It is very worthwhile to note that trying a few interfacing projects can be an excellent way to pick up some knowledge of electronics. The essence of electronics does not lie in Ohm's Law, it lies, instead, in ideas such as making "refined nature" work for or entertain us. Along the way, electronics contains many collections of knowledge and technical details. Learning about any subject is very largely the job of building up and maintaining enough enthusiasm to accomplish something, and such a journey will be full of occasions for learning.

If you are already able to write some simple programs, then you are already familiar with some of the concepts entailed in electronics, and your personal computer has become a very nice tool by which to explore electronics.

Types of Ins and Outs

First let's consider the types of inputs and outputs which might be useful, and how those can be implemented.

Fundamentally, there are a number of ways in which we can categorize inputs and outputs which will help provide an idea of the range of possibilities.

Digital or Analog?   The first characteristic is whether the I/O is a simple on/off (logic) type of signal, or it is continuous (analog), varying to any value within a certain range. An on/off input might originate at a switch, while an analog value might come from a sensor of some kind, perhaps light or temperature.

If the input comes from another intelligent device, bytes of information might need to be communicated, which might be communicated via a cable with 8 logic lines. An example of such a scheme is the cable from the computer to a parallel printer! Rarely, however, does the real world present information to us 8 bits at a time.

Outputs also may be digital or analog. A digital output might turn on or off a light or sound, while an analog output might control the brightness of a light or the loudness of a sound.

Fast or Slow?   How frequently is the input or output to be updated? Depending upon the rate, different electronics may be needed as well as different programming techniques.

Is "Power" Involved?   Often the devices to be controlled require a substantial amount of power to operate. In this case, any output from the computer can only be expected to *control* the power to the device, rather than powering the device directly. For example, a relay might be used so that the computer can control a lighting display.

What To Tackle, and How

It is really my object here to provide some quick-and-dirty techniques for using your computer's existing input/output capabilities for fun purposes. Some of these are the kinds of things you can do on a Sunday evening without even reaching for your credit card. Nonetheless, some extremely useful connections can be made.

However, there is no question that, for major projects, the best course of action is to obtain appropriate interface boards to do the job.

For computers with slots, cards are available which provide more digital input and output lines than you could probably use. For analog signals, a wide variety of cards is available offering different combinations of speed, precision, number of channels and, of course, price.

Some Applications Ideas

There are so many fun things that can be easily controlled by computers, but I have to admit a weakness for fancy lighting arrangements. You can also control model railroads, sensing where the trains are and responding accordingly. You can calculate sound waveforms and play them through your stereo.

Many pieces of stereo and video gear these days are completely controlled by (non-mechanical) pushbuttons, which you can connect up and control from a computer. If you are into fireworks, these too can be sequenced by computer. If computer games are your thing, why restrict yourself to keyboard and screen?

Obtaining Parts and Information

Doubtless, you will not need to be told that many of the parts referred to in the upcoming suggestions can be obtained at Radio Shack. Parts obtained there also generally come with some sort of connection diagram or pinout configurations.

However, Radio Shack is far from the only component supplier, and compared to many, has a very limited selection. Most cities have surplus dealers who carry some parts. Used parts are often not worth the saving, but unused surplus components, such as excess purchases from production runs, can be bargains. Next on the list are mail-order component companies, whose advertisements fill the back pages of electronics and computer magazines. Definitely order a catalog.

Finally, for very hard-to-get parts (of which I have listed none so far as I know) you can try the distributors where manufacturers go to get their parts. These folks differ in availability of catalogs, and willingness to deal with private customers, but it doesn't hurt to ask.

If you buy components anywhere but Radio Shack, then you will be missing the data sheets, which are especially nice to have for integrated circuits. This means that you need to be introduced to the wonderful world of data books. The electronics world runs on data books, and if you catch the electronics bug, you can spend a few dollars on data books and keep yourself entertained endlessly.

Most major component companies publish data books for their lines of integrated circuits, with separate books for logic or for linear circuits like amplifiers and timers. These are not books written by an independent author; these are the actual sources of information which everyone refers to in order to design anything. You will probably have most luck by perusing a mail-order component-supplier's catalog and ordering the data books which include those chips which look interesting. Be sure to get up-to-date ones, as they contain the most intriguing information on always improving component families.

Q & D Techniques

The basic ideas are simple: anywhere on the computer that there is an input or output is an opportunity for us to hook up something else. Yet, not all such opportunities are very worthwhile; for example, the disk-drive interface is a little complicated for us to take advantage of economically.

However, we have other opportunities:

Joystick Port: This contains several switch-type inputs, and on some computers also will read the resistance of potentiometers (or whatever kind of resistor we wish to use).

Printer Port: Eight logical outputs are available here. On some machines, such as the PC, there are also a number of inputs which can be used. Combining four inputs with eight outputs means we can actually sense 32 switches in a matrix, if necessary.

The Keyboard: Almost all commonly used keyboards (real IBM PC excepted) are simply arrays of switches. Nothing stops us from hooking up our own switches across those of the keyboard!

RS-232 Port: If there's an unused RS-232 port on your machine, it probably has at least one or two control wires which can be operated from software and become useful inputs or outputs.

Preparation

There are a couple of items of preparation which will probably be needed before plowing ahead.

First, you will need to obtain whatever documentation is available on the particular input or output you propose to use in this unorthodox fashion. This is the information which tells you which connector pins do what, and tells you about what memory or port address does what to control this connector. Most of these jobs will require familiarity with various "PEEKs" and "POKEs" if you are operating in BASIC, or a little assembler, if you are so inclined.

One very useful set of output wires is the printer port. However, if you are thinking of using that port, you usually can't just use PRINT statements. If you attempt to do that, the computer will send out a character, and then wait for the ready signal from the printer, which is disconnected. This being the case, you will need to send data directly to the port which controls the printer output.

Next, you will need a small amount of test gadgetry, so that you can confirm that your software experiments do what you think they should do. The test gadgetry is the trusty LED and beeper, similar to that used in previous chapters for testing RS-232 and MIDI interfaces.

You will also need a little skill at soldering connectors with a *delicate* iron, and maybe even a few chips. Please practice that skill if you feel it necessary!

Principles

The main principle is to make the new device that you will attach to the computer look electrically as similar as possible to the device that is normally attached. This is important to make the setup work, and also to make sure that no harm is done.

On the subject of harm, there is a good rule to keep in mind. *Never* attach any device to your computer which can generate a voltage which is out of the range your computer normally expects on that wire. For most inputs, that is a range of 0 volts to 5 volts. For RS-232 inputs *only*, you are allowed the range of plus or minus 12 volts. Make sure that you don't accidentally hook an RS-232 output to an ordinary TTL-logic (0 to 5-volt) input.

And, of course, make sure that TTL outputs from the computer are never shorted to ground or +5 volts, and that you don't inadvertently mistake outputs for inputs and attempt to feed a signal into an output.

OK, stop sweating and let's get down to business!

Simple Switch Inputs

Switch inputs are easy. Anywhere there is a digital input, we can hook up a switch. If the input is *intended* to accept a switch input (for example, if it is used with a joystick) then it may have an internal pull-up resistor, and all that is necessary is to hook the switch between the input and ground. This is shown in Figure 21-1.

If there is no internal pull-up, then you have to arrange an external one, as in Figures 21-2 or 21-3.

Optoisolator (Optocoupler) Input

In some cases, it may be desirable to electrically isolate the input circuit from the computer. This may be the case if you are not sure what voltages are present on the inputting device.

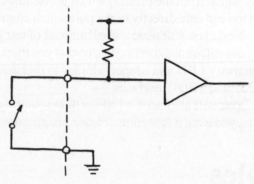

Figure 21-1   A diagram of a simple switch hook-up for input which is intended for use with switches and thus has an internal pull-up resistor.

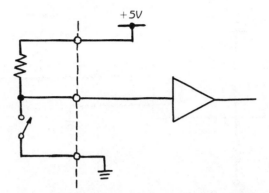

Figure 21-2 If 5 volts is readily available on the computer's connector, then it can be used for the pull-up job. The resistor can be any value from 1 kohm to 20 kohm or more.

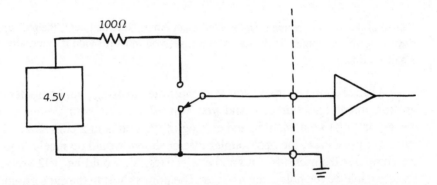

Figure 21-3 If 5 volts is not readily available, then a 4.5-volt battery can be used to provide either a pull-up voltage, or the high logic voltage as shown here. This is slightly preferable to using the battery attached to a pull-up resistor (as in Figure 21-2) because, when the switch is closed, the battery will be draining. We don't care too much if we drain the 5-volt supply a little.

Figure 21-4 shows the use of an *optocoupler*. An optocoupler is merely an LED plus a phototransistor in the same package. If the LED is lit, the phototransistor conducts and, in this case, acts like a switch pulling down the input signal voltage.

The LED section of the optocoupler can be powered from any source which will supply enough current. This can be calculated using Ohm's law. Typically, you need to arrange at least 10 milliamps to 20 millamps of current. V1 in our diagram must be attached to the more positive voltage, and don't forget that there will be about 1.5 volts across the LED.

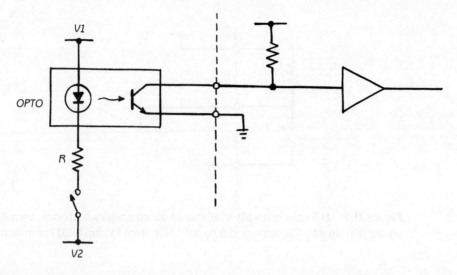

Figure 21-4 An optocoupler can be used as an input. Note that here, the pull-up is shown internal to the computer. If this is not the case, you must provide it externally. 5 kohms would be fine.

As an example, suppose you were interested in using your computer as a tune-up instrument for your car, and you wanted to feed your computer a signal corresponding to the opening and closing of the points in a conventional-ignition system. In that case, the optocoupler circuit shown would do nicely, and protects the computer from unruly automotive electrics. V1 would be +12 volts, and the switch would be the points themselves. The points short to the car's ground, which corresponds to V2 in our diagram.

The voltage across the optocoupler-plus-resistor when the points are closed will be +12 volts, and across the resistor there will be about 10.5 volts. To arrange a current of 10 millamps we need a resistor of about 1000 ohms.

Optocouplers are rated in terms of how much current the output section will draw compared to how much input current is passed through the LED. If the LED is supplied with 10 millamps, and this causes the output transistor to draw only 1 milliamps this is said to be a transfer ratio of 10 percent.

Some readily available optocoupler are: 4N28 (transfer ratio 10%), 4N31 (50%) and 4N33 (500%).

Optical Input

A similar case is the use of a phototransistor by itself as an input. This can be used to detect whether it is light in the room. Or, the phototransistor can detect interruptions in a beam of light. This might be used to detect the passing of a model train, count bottles on a production line or the entry of people through a doorway, or to detect the transparent leader on recording tape.

Heartbeat Monitor

The schematic of a heart-beat monitor is shown in Figure 21-5. Although it appears to involve a large number of amplifiers, these come four to an IC, and the whole circuit is actually quite compact and easy to build.

LED1 supplies infra-red light, some of which passes through the subject's earlobe and is picked up by phototransistor Q1. These two components can be mounted on some sort of clip — a modified clothes-peg works well. In addition, other parts of the body can be used, such as fingers or lips.

The phototransitor's collector connection should be attached via shielded wire to the rest of the circuit to avoid picking up 60-hertz noise. Op-amps 1a and 1b amplify the weak light-fluctuation signal to an amplitude of over 2 volts at the output of 1b. Comparator 2a compares those fluctuations to a mid-level voltage, and signals a high or low to the computer. That output is also routed to comparator 2b which lights an LED with the pulses to provide immediate verification of operation.

Comparators 2c and 2d operate 2 LEDs which assist in adjusting variable resistor RV. This control is used to adjust the operation of the phototransistor to a point where it is just starting to turn on, but not too much. That point will vary between transistors and also depend on the brightness of the LED. To some extent, the particular ear will also affect this adjustment.

CMOS amplifiers and comparators are specified for this project because they operate happily with only a 5-volt supply.

Many of the capacitors shown have 0.1 and 0.2 microfarad values. These values are readily available, but often only in physically-large sizes. Small ones are sold for use in filtering the power fed to the chips in computers, and may be seen dotting most computer boards. If you can locate a source for such small capacitors the project will be more compact. If you have trouble finding the 0.2 microfarad value, simply use two 0.1 microfarad capacitors in parallel. In addition, the resistor values are very non-critical, and substituting other values within 10 or even 20 percent will work just as well.

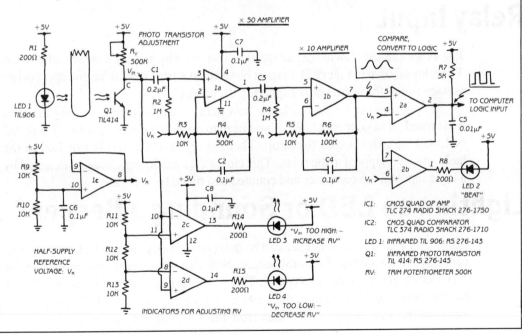

Figure 21-5   A heartbeat detector for earlobe is shown. An LED provides the light, and a phototransistor observes the opacity of an ear-lobe, signalling the computer of the occurrence of a heartbeat.

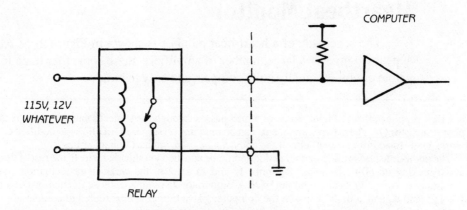

Figure 21-6   A relay can be used to inform the computer of some event.

The sensitivity of the phototransistor depends, of course, upon the model of the phototransistor, but also very much on the pull-up resistor value. The phototransistor draws current in proportion to the amount of light hitting it. Therefore, if you use a very low value of pull-up (say 200 ohms), this will require a very bright light to pull down sufficiently. If you use a high value (say 20 kohms), a dimmer light will pull down the the input signal voltage. Figure 21-5 shows an amplified phototransistor in use as a heart-beat detector.

Relay Input

Just as we can use a switch as an input, so we can also use the contacts of a relay. The relay (shown in Figure 21-6) must be selected so that its coil has the appropriate voltage rating for whatever is supplying the power.

Supposing you wished to know how many times and for how long the light was turned on in your room. What you need to do is find a relay with a 115-volt AC coil, and wire that across the lamp. Then, every time 115 volt is supplied to the lamp, it's also suppled to the relay. This closes the switch, which can be detected by a logic input on the computer and counted and timed by software.

Lighting an LED or Sounding a Beeper

Either an LED or a piezo beeper can be powered directly from a TTL output, and certainly from an RS-232 control output. Note that when supplying power from a TTL output, it is preferable to use the TTL gate to pull down, since that is where it has the most capability. Thus, the LED in Figure 21-7 is connected between +5 volts and the TTL output, rather than from the TTL output to ground.

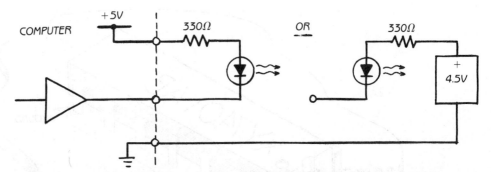

Figure 21-7 Here an ordinary TTL output is used to light an LED. If 5 volts is not available, then an external 4.5-volt battery pack will do.

Obtaining Some Power

If +5volts is not brought out to your computer's connectors somewhere, then you may want to bring it out yourself. With the aid of a meter, it is pretty easy to find a source of 5 volts inside the machine, even without a schematic.

Most of the smaller (14-pin to 20-pin) chips inside will have numbers with a 74 at the beginning of the numeric part, like "AB74LS10XY". These chips are very consistently designed so that +5 volts is supplied to the highest-numbered pin, and ground is supplied to the pin diagonally opposite. Figure 21-8 shows how to locate these pins, and +5 volts.

In addition, if your computer has an RS-232 interface, it may also have a source of +12 volts and −12 volts. Figure 21-9 shows where to locate those voltages.

Having found a desired voltage, you can carefully wire on to it, preferably on the PC circuit board rather than on a chip leg. Bring the wire to an unused pin on some connector. An RS-232 connector is a good choice, but stay clear of the commonly used pins. Be careful to ensure that your new power-supply wire is unlikely to be shorted to ground, or to other points in the circuit.

When using a power supply voltage outside the computer, it is a good idea to put a resistor in the line any time that an exact voltage is *not* needed. Thus, if 5 volts is simply being used at some remote point to pull up some switches, stick a 200-ohm (or so) resistor in the line near the computer. This way, if the 5-volt line does get itself into trouble, it won't short the supply and bomb the computer. On the other hand, if the +5 volts is to be used for powering logic chips, then you will have to run a wire direct, and just be sure that it can't get into danger.

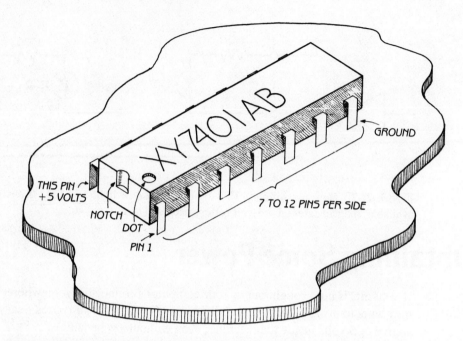

Figure 21-8   Pin numbering is shown for typical TTL chips, and their connection to power and ground.

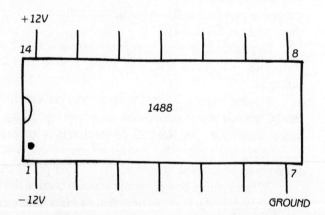

Figure 21-9   A large proportion of RS-232 interfaces use the trusty old 1488/75188 driver for sending. This gives us a clue as to where to find plus and minus 12 volts.

Switching a Relay

Relays are rated on four main characteristics:

- Minimum voltage required across the coil to switch the contacts.
- Amount of coil current necessary to switch the contacts.

- Maximum current the contacts can carry when closed.

- Maximum voltage permitted across contacts when open.

Only the most delicate relays can be switched directly by a TTL output. These would be suitable for merely switching another signal, or for wiring across a switch in some other equipment which is known to carry very little current.

For switching larger amounts of power, the arrangement in Figure 21-10 is appropriate. Here, a power transistor is used to switch the power to the relay coil, which, in turn, switches a completely independent power circuit (which could be anything from a low voltage circuit up to 115-volt AC, presuming the appropriate relay is selected.)

When a transistor is used as a switch, its operation is relatively simple. There are two sexes of transistor, and I will limit this discussion to the type called "NPN."

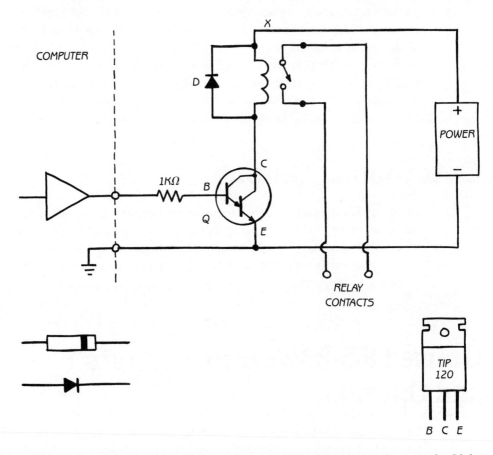

Figure 21-10   A computer output is used to switch a relay and thereby control a high-power device. The transistor can be any of a variety of NPN Darlingtons, of which TIP120 is easily obtainable. The diode can be one of the 1N400X series (1N4001 to 1N4008, etc). Select the relay based upon the four criteria listed in the text.

The transistor has three terminals: Base, Emitter and Collector. For our purpose, the emitter is connected to ground. All we have to do is arrange for a current into the base, and the transistor will turn on and draw current into the collector.

Effectively, we can view the collector as a switch to ground, and feeding a current into the base controls that switch. Typically, the collector current can be up to 100 times the controlling base current. If it would be higher than that, then the transistor no longer operates as merely a fully-turned-on switch and we actually have to resort to mathematics to find out what is happening.

In Figure 21-10, the transistor shown is a special dual transistor, known as a *Darlington*. This configuration is more ideal for our purpose, because, with two transistors, we can switch a collector current of around 1000 to 5000 times the base current! This being the case, we only need a very small base current to switch a relatively large collector current.

In this case, the relay coil would be chosen to match the power source. This power source could be the computer's +5-volt or +12-volt supply if sufficient current is available, or an external supply (perhaps there are many relays hooked up, instead of just one).

The rectifier D appears at first to do nothing, however it is needed when the transistor turns off. At that instant, the magnetic energy stored in the relay coil is released back into electrical form, which would generate a potentially damaging pulse of high voltage. The rectifier safely conducts this pulse.

Optocoupler Output

Figure 21-11 shows an example using an optocoupler on a computer output. This particular example concerns using the optocoupler to switch a transistor which, in turn, switches a relay. This particular circuit might come in handy if the relay-coil power is externally available, but it is desired that no direct electrical connection be made to the computer.

Unused RS-232 Control Inputs and Outputs

On many computers, the RS-232 interface has some control lines (i.e., *not* data lines) which are accessible directly from software. Chapter 9 on RS-232 Monitoring Gadgets already shows how to hook up an LED or beeper to such an output. Figures 21-12 and 21-13 show how to drive a relay, and to input a switch to RS-232 lines.

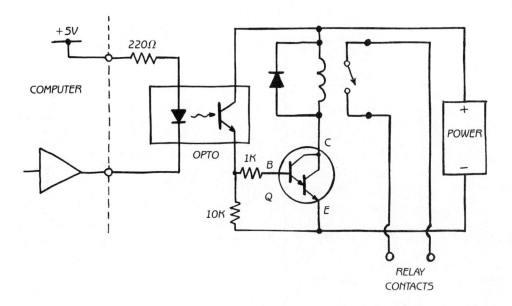

Figure 21-11 Similar to Figure 21-10, however an optocoupler is used to switch the Darlington transistor, which permits the relay coil power to be completely unconnected from the computer.

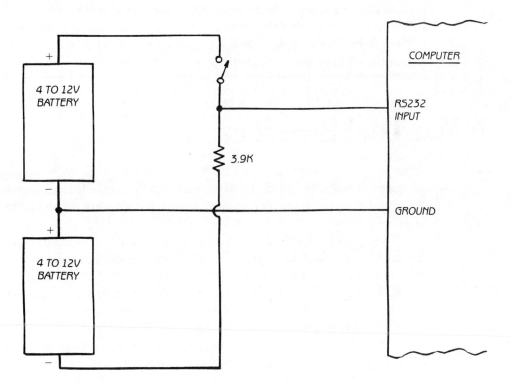

Figure 21-12 Hooking a switch to an RS-232 control input.

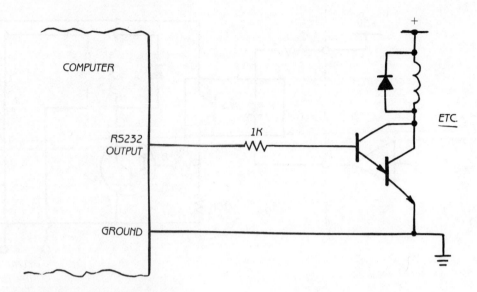

Figure 21-13 Using an RS-232 control output to control the transistor which switches the relay. . . just like in Figure 21-10.

A word of caution: while it is easy to hook up devices to RS-232 lines, it may be disproportionately difficult to figure out the software necessary to get at those lines. You may need to delve quite deeply into a technical manual in order to find out the necessary codes and port locations.

A Matrix of Switches

When a large number of switches or push buttons must be watched by the computer, it would be inefficient to connect each individually to a separate input. Instead, it is common practice to use a matrix arrangement, as shown in Figure 21-14.

Described here is the principle of the matrix: software starts by raising all of the output port's lines to "high." The software loops around, making each output line low in turn. On each loop, the software reads the input port, looking for any of the bits being low (zero). If, for example, on the second loop Bit 0 was found to be low, this would tell the software that the switch at Row 1 Column zero was pushed.

This scheme works fine so long as only one switch is pushed at a time. In fact, most computer keyboards operate this way. However, if more than one key is pushed, then it is usually not possible to determine which keys had been pushed. If it is necessary to detect more than one switch at a time, then use a diode in series with the switch, as shown (note orientation). The diode should be a germanium

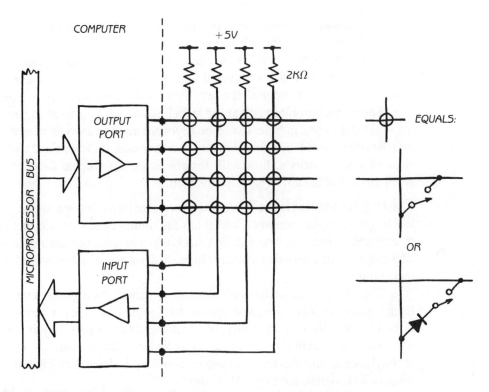

Figure 21-14   Circuitry for reading a matrix of switches showing that at each intersection, a switch is located.

type, such as 1N34A. Silicon types, such as 1N4148, will not work because, when conducting, they have a voltage across them of about 0.7 volt, as opposed to 0.3 volt for the germanium types. This would cause the scanned-switch signal to fall outside the zero input range of the input port.

The Computer's Own Keyboard

Having seen how to scan some added-on switches, why not simply wire switches across the existing switches in the keyboard? This is quite an acceptable idea, and your software then just has to ask for input from the keyboard! There are a couple of difficulties though...

First, there are some keyboards which don't use actual switches with contacts. Some use capacitive switches, which depend on sensing the position of each key in somewhat the same way as the high-class, no-moving-parts elevator buttons on some fancy buildings. Some real IBM PC keyboards fall into this class. Others have tiny magnets on the bottom of each key, whose proximity is detected by a semiconductor magnetic field detector chip called a *Hall effect sensor*.

Determining whether your keyboard has simple ordinary switches can be done with an ohmmeter. While you are at it, you will notice that (on most keyboards) each keyswitch has four legs. Usually, these are connected in pairs. Perhaps Pins 1 and 2 are connected together, and Pins 3 and 4 are connected together. Then when you push the key, Pins 1 and 2 are connected to 3 and 4.

The second problem is that the switches you wire up need to behave like a typist. That is to say, in order to use the keyboard input you would need the external switches to be closed only for relatively short periods. If the external switch will be closed for long periods, how will this affect the auto-repeat function. Will the keyboard buffer fill up? What happens then?

Faking Keyswitches: In some cases you might have a signal you would like to feed into the computer, and it has the timing characteristic of a typist—in other words, a short "on" period. But this is a logic signal and not a switch closure. This can be dealt with using a handy chip called a 4066, which is part of the CMOS logic family.

The 4066 provides what look like four switches which are each turned on by a logic high on an input line, and opened by a logic low. This is shown in Figure 21-15. Note that the CMOS family, of which the 4066 is a part, requires at least 3.3 volts for a logic high (when the supply is 5 volts). Since ordinary TTL families normally are a little short in this respect, a pull-up resistor (1 to 2 kohm) should be used on TTL signals feeding CMOS inputs.

Resistor Input

If the phenomenon to be sensed can be detected with a resistive sensor, then there is a good possibility that such a sensor could hook on to a joystick port, if your computer normally uses potentiometer joysticks. It will be necessary to detemine the normal range of resistance in the real joystick potentiometers, and attempt to obtain a sensor with a comparable range as shown in Figure 21-16.

Both light and temperature are amenable to this approach using a resistive photocell for light or a thermistor for temperature. However, in both cases you will need to perform some calibration, and neither type of component is very linear, so the range of numbers generated for the span of interest may not be very large.

Analog Output

Figure 21-17 shows the most complicated endeavor of this chapter, a rudimentary digital-to-analog converter which can run off the printer port. The 74HCT245 is used simply as a buffer. The HCT family is relatively new, and is rather nice in that it is CMOS and therefore low power, but runs as fast as the LSTTL family used in most personal computers, and contains most of the familiar TTL types.

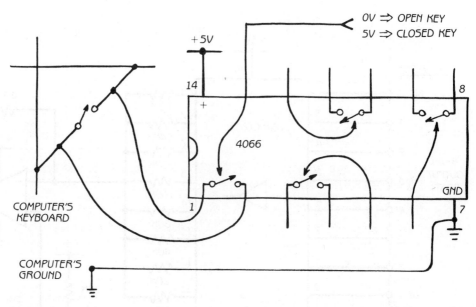

Figure 21-15   Illustration of how a 4066 can be used to "convert" a logic signal to a fake switch closure.

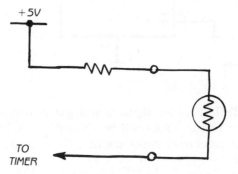

Figure 21-16   Attaching a resistive sensor to a computer's potentiometer-style joystick port.

It is specified here for one of its other attributes—its inputs work fine directly from TTL (which is what we have at the printer port), yet, unlike TTL, its outputs swing from 0 volt for low, to 5 volts for high.

The outputs from the 74HCT245 are added together by the resistors and op-amp which follow. (The actual theory behind the op-amp is covered in many electronics books.) Each bit is added in with a different weighting (note the ratios of two); the higher the resistor, the lower the weighting. Also, the op-amp inverts the result with respect to 2.5 volts. Sending a byte value of 128 (1000 0000 binary) to the port will produce an output of about 2.5 volts, while 0 (0000 0000) will produce about 5 volts, and 255 (1111 1111) comes up with about 0 volt.

This is not the all-around best way to implement a digital-to-analog converter. In fact, D to A chips are available which do the job all in one package, and much more accurately. However this does make visible exactly what a D to A does.

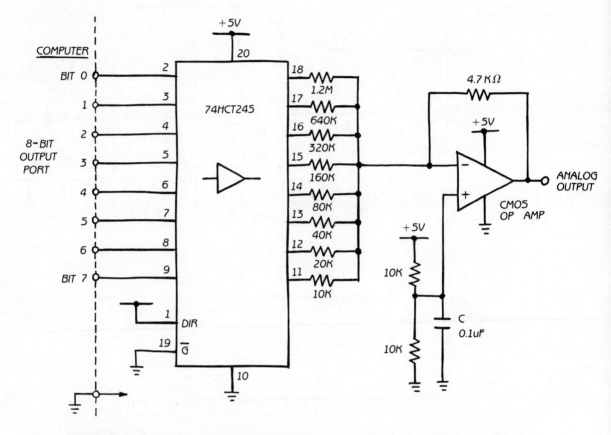

Figure 21-17 An 8-bit, digital-to-analog converter, just to demonstrate the principle. Not all of the resistor values will be obtainable exactly. In that case make them up with combinations of other values in series. The op-amp can be any CMOS type, for example TLC 271.

Analog Input (of Sorts)

Analog inputs can be implemented using a digital-to-analog converter, plus a component called a *comparator*. A comparator simply compares the voltage on its two inputs and gives a high output if the plus input is higher than the minus input.

We can use the D to A converter to supply a reference voltage to the minus input of the comparator, and the analog input signal of interest goes to the other comparator input. The output of the comparator feeds into a TTL input. Then, we simply have the software increment the D to A until the reference is greater than the input signal, which is being watched at an input line. Thus the software finds out the voltage of the analog input.

A four-channel version of this is shown in Figure 21-18. That number was picked simply because the most readily available comparators are the LM339 and

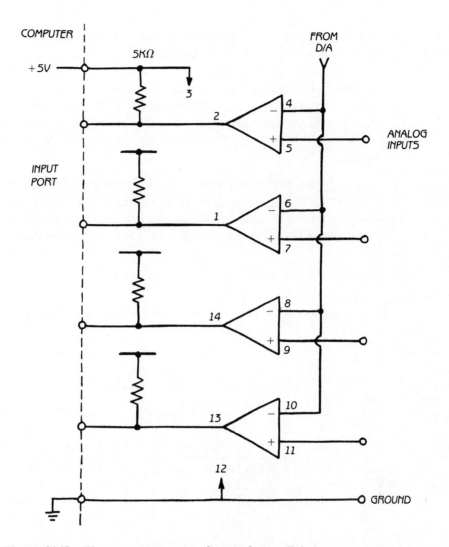

Figure 21-18 The comparator part of an analog-to-digital converter using the D to A converter of Figure 21-17. The comparator is an LM339 or TLC374.

its low-power counterpart, the TLC374, which are both quad units. Since we can feed the same D to A reference to all four sections, we get three extra channels for free.

Notes:

- First, as shown in Figure 21-18, the analog inputs must be in the range 0 to 5 volts. If a larger range is needed, it can be attenuated using a resistive divider.

- The accuracy of the A to D obviously depends on the accuracy of the D to A.

- The speed of the A to D conversion depends on how fast you can determine the number where the D to A is *just* greater (or less than) the analog input. The simple-minded approach would be to simply count the D to A up until it is greater than the analog input, which might take up to 255 steps. However, a more rapid approach entails setting each bit high in turn (starting with the most significant). If that exceeds the analog input, then it is set back to zero. Otherwise, it is left high. In this way, the number is determined in only 8 steps.

- Again, there are one-chip, analog to digital converters which you simply tell to convert and they come up with the number by themselves. However, the output from one of these will require 8 input lines into the computer, which starts to look like it needs an interface card to plug into one of its slots.

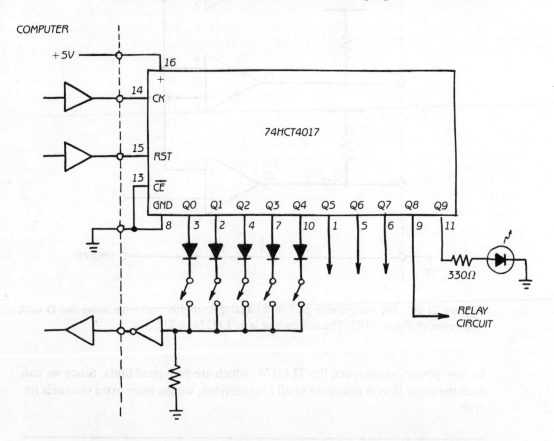

Figure 21-19 Using a CMOS 4017 to expand the number of output lines. If possible, use a 74HCT4017. Otherwise an "ordinary" 4017 will do, but will need pull-up resistors (1 to 2 kohm OK) on the two lines which drive the 4017's CK and RST inputs.

Output Expansion Using Counters

Just to take things to the limit, if you really want a lot of outputs and your computer has only two or three to spare, you can use counter chips to boost that number. Shown in Figure 21-19 is an example. Here a CMOS 4017 is used to simulate multiple outputs. The 4017 has 10 output lines numbered 0 to 9, of which only one is high at a time. One of the computer's outputs is used to clock the 4017, incrementing the selection of high output. The other computer output is used to reset the chip back to zero.

An assortment of items are shown attached. Adding a CMOS inverter or buffer allows us to read a number of switches, whose value is checked one by one and fed into a computer input. The diodes on the 4017 outputs to the switches can be 1N4148s or other signal diodes. If only one switch will be closed at a time, then the diodes are not required. Two other 4017 outputs are shown driving an LED and a relay circuit (steal design from previous example).

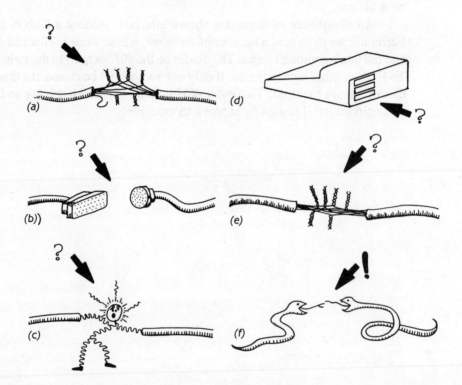

SKILLS TEST #27

IDENTIFY THE
STANDARD INTERFACE(S)

(a)

(d)

(b))

(e)

(c)

(f)

22

Loose Ends

As usual, time marches onwards. Ever more sophisticated computer devices keep arriving, and with them, a share of interconnection puzzles. But the principles for solving those puzzles remain the same. Sort out all of the details needed to get the information communicated properly. Then, find out how to attend to those details, and how to test each stage if possible. Find out what tools are available to let you see what is going on.

I conclude this book with a few notes on possible future interconnection challenges, fed by some of the more recent events.

RS-422, etc.

Some would have us believe that RS-232 should one day be superseded by RS-422, which is the reason that the Mac has an RS-422 connector, and why several other machines have RS-422 as an option. Should we start worrying, yet?

It is not yet clear that RS-422 will catch on as a popular interface for personal computer equipment. Since the same chips and connector which implement an RS-422 interface can also implement an RS-232 interface, any machine with RS-422 will also have RS-232. Consequently, this aspect provides little motivation for peripheral manufacturers to build RS-422 products, which might have boosted the popularity of RS-422 on the computer end.

A factor which would bring RS-422 into popularity is the necessity for rapid data communication, such as for graphics printing, and especially for connection to laser printers. Yet, even the Apple Laser Writer provides an RS-232 port along with the Appletalk network connection.

Meanwhile, networks are filling some of the high-speed data needs, and help to share the expensive high-data-rate peripherals amongst multiple users. And, if that is not enough, we also have optical fiber interconnection schemes on the horizon, which provide high speed communication rates over reasonable distances with no susceptibility to, or generation of electrical interference.

Local Area Networks

Networks seem an obvious subject of investigation while on the topic of interconnections. However, it appears that networks do not need or yield to the sort of techniques which have been the subject of this book.

In the first place, networks are somewhat more complicated combinations of hardware and software operating together. As a result, the network manufacturer is obliged to take care of the details which make the network go. But the purchaser is also obliged; he must buy network components which are either from the same manufacturer, or are guaranteed to work together.

Consequently, there does not seem to be this grey area where multitudes of different manufacturers are producing devices which might work together so long as the purchaser applies some technical expertise, as occurs with RS-232, Centronics and video products.

Therefore, you either become a network expert and work in the field of networking, or you simply buy the network complete and stay out of the technical details. The technical details do not help you to make things work better, except, perhaps, fundamental details like "how fast does it run" and "can I run this software with it."

New Video Schemes

The trend toward higher resolution video continues. This is reinforced by the crash in memory prices. High-resolution video is very hungry for memory: a 1k by 1k by 256-color display (which is very pretty) consumes 1 megabyte of memory. This once cost a fortune. Now it would be a small fraction of a system's cost.

Personal computers have really exceeded the limit of what can be displayed on monitors which obey TV-style standards. So, along with higher resolution, expect to see an increase in the number of non-standard video monitors. For a time, this will mean that many computer systems can only be used with specific monitors, and interchangeability will be reduced. We have already seen this in the Mac, and the Atari 520 ST, along with the IBM PC's monochrome monitor, and the newer enhanced and professional graphics adapters.

Small Computer System Interface: SCSI

Several computers, including the Atari ST series and the Mac Plus, have appeared recently with SCSI interfaces. This is initially a standard for attaching hard disk drives. However, since it is a general interface for rapid parallel data transfer, it could quite easily be used for communication to devices other than a hard disk drive. The possibilities are intriguing, but little practical experience has yet been gained as to how these interfaces will really be used (and may be further abused by us), so SCSI exploration will have to be passed over in this book.

Apple's Mini-Circular Connectors

In a continuing quest for connectors which consume less rear-panel space, Apple has introduced yet another variety of connector. In Apple literature, it is referred to as a Mini-Circular connector and resembles a shrunken DIN-type audio connector.

Figure 22-1 shows a greatly expanded view of the socket (female) as it appears on the rear panel of the Mac Plus, and also on other peripherals such as Apple's Imagewriter II. The accompanying table shows the relationship between signals on the Mini-Circular and those on the older DB-9.

The cable which is used to join a Mac to an Imagewriter II is not a straight-through cable. Connections are swapped around so that outputs and inputs are found in the same place on both the computer and the printer. The swaps might be thought of as a mirror image about a vertical axis. The connected pins are: A-B, B-A, C-E, E-C, F-H, H-F, D-D, G-G.

Apple dealers supply various adapter cables for connecting between Mini-Circular-equipped devices and others with DB-9s or DB-25s. At this writing, no source has appeared for raw connector parts suitable for hand assembly. It is always possible, however, to chop up one end of a molded cable and attach your own connector.

One problem has surfaced with the Mini-Circular connectors when they are used with a DB-9 adapter to connect to certain small peripherals. Some serial-to-parallel and MIDI interface boxes draw their power from the 5-volt connection on the DB-9. This 5-volt supply is not provided on the Mini-Circular socket, and hence is unavailable to the peripheral. Manufacturers of such interface boxes have had to devise other ways of obtaining power.

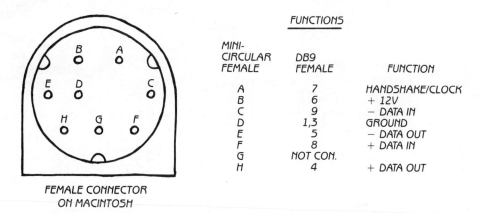

MINI-CIRCULAR FEMALE	DB9 FEMALE	FUNCTION
A	7	HANDSHAKE/CLOCK
B	6	+ 12V
C	9	– DATA IN
D	1,3	GROUND
E	5	– DATA OUT
F	8	+ DATA IN
G	NOT CON.	
H	4	+ DATA OUT

FEMALE CONNECTOR
ON MACINTOSH

Figure 22-1   An expanded view of the (female) socket as it appears on the rear panel of the Mac Plus and other peripherals.

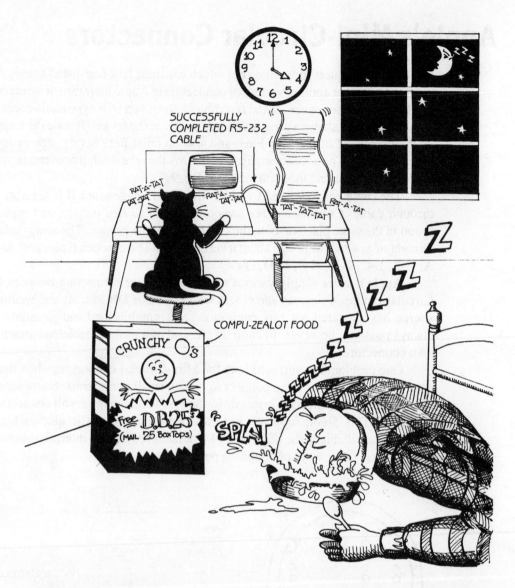

SUCCESSFULLY COMPLETED RS-232 CABLE

RAT-A-TAT TAT TAT

RAT-A-TAT-TAT

TAT-TAT-TAT

RAT-A-TAT

COMPU-ZEALOT FOOD

CRUNCHY O'S

Free D.B.25
(MAIL 25 BOX TOPS)

SPLAT

After many hours of Diligent Labor, Frank had completed the job, and found himself with . . . Cereal In Da Face!!!

Appendix

ASCII: Is It Really as Boring as People Say?

ASCII stands for American Standard Code for Information Interchange, and is the almost universally used system for representing characters inside a computer as bytes or numbers-codes. Knowing about ASCII is useful at many times—from understanding what your programs are doing when they send characters to screen or printer, to figuring out how to send special codes to the printer or receiving special codes from your keyboard.

It should be mentioned, however, that much of the interesting stuff about sending codes hither and thither comes from different manufacturer's *extensions* to ASCII. For example, ordinary ASCII defines what the first 128 byte values represent, leaving 128 free. In addition, some of the first 128 codes are used for control purposes (such as carriage return). The IBM-PC uses ASCII to choose the characters which will be displayed on the screen but doesn't stop at the ASCII set only. All 256 codes have some sort of character shape attached, including some foreign characters, shapes used for drawing boxes, and miscellaneous other shapes.

This same scheme is used by almost all personal computer systems, although the non-character shapes are not the same from manufacturer to manufacturer.

Following, for what it's worth, is a list of the ordinary ASCII codes. Each entry has a decimal and hexadecimal number for the code, followed by information about how that code may be generated by a keyboard, what character the code may represent, or the name it has, or what action a terminal or printer may perform upon receiving that code.

The Control Codes

The first 32 codes do not represent visible characters, but instead were designated to signal control functions for teletypes and tape machines and readers. Only a few of these codes continue to be used for their original purposes, and consequently, the original names for many of these codes no longer have meaning.

Hex	Dec	Name(s)	Keyboard Key
0	0	NUL	Control-@

This code may be used to "pad" messages. It is a do-nothing character which receiving devices often are supposed to ignore. This is useful if it is necessary to send something, but the receiver will not be ready to do anything about it.

Hex	Dec	Name(s)	Keyboard Key
1	1	SOH "Start of Header"	Control-A
2	2	STX "Start of Text"	Control-B
3	3	ETX "End of Text"	Control-C

Control-C is a keyboard character which is often used to interrupt and quit whatever operation the computer may be performing, such as displaying a directory or executing a program. This is true of many versions of BASIC and other languages, and is built in to many operating systems from micros to mainframes.

Hex	Dec	Name(s)	Keyboard Key
4	4	EOT "End of Transmission"	Control-D
5	5	ENQ "Enquiry"	Control-E
6	6	ACK "Acknowledge"	Control-F
7	7	BEL	Control-G
		Control-G Rings a bell or beeper.	
8	8	Back Space	Control-H
9	9	Horizontal Tab	Control-I
0A	10	Line Feed	Control-J
0B	11	Vertical Tab	Control-K
0C	12	Form Feed	Control-L
0D	13	Carriage Return	Control-M

Note that many devices such as printers and terminals do not automatically go to the next line when they receive a Carriage Return, but merely return to the beginning of the present line. For this reason, it is usually necessary to start a new line by sending the sequence Carriage Return followed by Line Feed.

0E	14	SO "Shift Out"	Control-N
0F	15	SI "Shift In"	Control-O
10	16	DLE "Data Line Escape"	Control-P

On a number of systems, particularly those running MSDOS/PCDOS or CP/M operating systems, keying Control-P will activate a software switch which sends all screen output to the printer as well.

| 11 | 17 | DC1 "Device Control 1" | Control-Q |

In many situations Control-S may reverse the effect of Control-Q (see below).

| 12 | 18 | DC2 | Control-R |
| 13 | 19 | DC3 | Control-S |

This character is used in the "X-ON X-OFF" flow-control scheme (see the RS-232 section for more details). On many systems, this character sent from the keyboard has the effect of halting the screen output, until Control-Q is keyed.

14	20	DC4	Control-T
15	21	NAK "Negative Acknowledge"	Control-U
16	22	SYN "Synchronous Idle"	Control-V
17	23	ETB "End of Transmission Block"	Control-W
18	24	CAN "Cancel"	Control-X
19	25	EM "End of Medium"	Control-Y
1A	26	SUB "Substitute"	Control-Z

In many situations, Control-Z is used to indicate the end of text. This applies to many word processors, to CP/M text files and to MSDOS text in certain situations (for example in the COPY utility where text is expected).

| 1B | 27 | ESC "Escape" | Control-[|

Escape is used as the starting character in many special, non-ASCII code sequences whose meaning varies from manufacturer to manufacturer (see section on escape sequences in Chapter 10).

1C	28	FS "File Separator"	Control-backslash
1D	29	GS "Group Separator"	Control-]
1E	30	RS "Record Separator"	Control-caret
1F	31	US "Unit Separator"	Control-underline

Visible Characters

20	32	Space		3D	61	=
21	33	!		3E	62	>
22	34	"		3F	63	?
23	35	#		40	64	@
24	36	$		41	65	A
25	37	%		42	66	B
26	38	&		43	67	C
27	39	'		44	68	D
28	40	(		45	69	E
29	41	)		46	70	F
2A	42	*		47	71	G
2B	43	+		48	72	H
2C	44	,		49	73	I
2D	45	–		4A	74	J
2E	46	.		4B	75	K
2F	47	/		4C	76	L
30	48	0		4D	77	M
31	49	1		4E	78	N
32	50	2		4F	79	O
33	51	3		50	80	P
34	52	4		51	81	Q
35	53	5		52	82	R
36	54	6		53	83	S
37	55	7		54	84	T
38	56	8		55	85	U

39	57	9		6C	108	l
3A	58	:		6D	109	m
3B	59	;		6E	110	n
3C	60	<		6F	111	o
5C	92	backslash		70	112	p
5D	93	]		71	113	q
5E	94	caret		72	114	r
5F	95	underline		73	115	s
60	96	`		74	116	t
61	97	a		75	117	u
62	98	b		76	118	v
63	99	c		77	119	w
64	100	d		78	120	x
65	101	e		79	121	y
66	102	f		7A	122	z
67	103	g		7B	123	Left curly bracket
68	104	h		7C	124	Stile
69	105	i		7D	125	Right curly bracket
6A	106	j		7E	126	Tilde
6B	107	k		7F	127	DELete

From the keyboard, DEL is generally interpreted by software to mean "delete something." When sent to a terminal, this may cause a blob to appear on the screen (ie: it's seen as a character, not a control code).

"ASCII" Text Files

The term "ASCII Text File" would literally mean a file which contains text using ASCII as the coding scheme for the characters. However, it has come to mean something more than that.

On many computers, whether micro or mainframe, there is a convention as to the format of files which contain text which certain system utility programs will be able to read. These system utilities may be the familiar CP/M or MSDOS TYPE command which displays a text file on the screen, a print utility, language compilers and assemblers, and batch-file processors.

To be sure, it is necessary for the text in such files to be ASCII, in other words, "A" must be decimal 65, and so on. However, there are other requirements, the principal one being that the file must be *line oriented*. That is to say, at the end of each line of text, a Carriage Return Line Feed sequence must appear. And in addition, there will probably be a limit as to how long each line may be.

Such a file is sometimes known by a more accurate name, *System Text File*, since it is a file which conforms to the needs of system utilities.

Needless to say, many word-processors do *not* normally put out files of System format. They make special use of many non-visible characters, to encode underline and super and subscript instructions, plus formatting details. There may also be sections of the file which contain non-textual configuration information. However, most word-processors are equipped with a mode which will write out a System ("ASCII") format file. For example, WordStar calls this "Non-Document mode."

RS-232 Testing Chart

Equipment: _____Date: _____

Pin Number	Official Name	Hi R Test	Lo R Test	In or Out	Function
1	Chassis Gnd				
2	Tx Data				
3	Rx Data				
4	RTS				
5	CTS				
6	DSR				
7	Signal Gnd				
8	RLSD				
9					
10					
11					
12	SRLDS				
13	SCTS				
14	STxD				
15	TSETDCE				
16	SRxD				
17	RSETDCE				
18					
19	SRTS				
20	DTR				
21	SQD				
22	RI				
23	DSRS				
24	TSETDTE				
25					

Index

MORE
FROM
SAMS

☐ Printer Connections Bible
Kim G. House and Jeff Marble, The Waite Group
At last, a book that includes extensive diagrams specifying exact wiring, DIP-switch settings and external printer details; a Jump Table of assorted printer/computer combinations; instructions on how to make your own cables; and reviews of various printers and how they function.
ISBN: 0-672-22406-2, $16.95

☐ Modem Connections Bible
Carolyn Curtis and Daniel L. Majhor, The Waite Group
Describes modems, how they work, and how to hook 10 well-known modems to 9 name-brand microcomputers. A handy Jump Table shows where to find the connection diagram you need and applies the illustrations to 11 more computers and 7 additional modems. Also features an overview of communications software, a glossary of communications terms, an explanation of the RS-232C interface, and a section on troubleshooting.
ISBN: 0-672-22446-1, $16.95

☐ Programmer's Guide to Asynchronous Communications   *Joe Campbell*
For intermediate and advanced programmers this book provides the history and technical details of asynchronous serial communications. Upon this foundation Campbell builds the specifics for the technical programmer, with an emphasis on popular UARTS and pseudo assembly language code.
ISBN: 0-672-22450-X, $21.95

☐ Data Communications, Networks, and Systems   *Thomas C. Bartee, Editor-in-Chief*
A comprehensive overview of state-of-the-art communications systems, operations, and new options are open to system users, written by experts in each given technology. Learn the advantages and disadvantages of local area networks; how modems, multiplexers and concentrators operate; the characteristics of fiber optics and coaxial cables; the forces shaping the structure and regulation of common carrier operations.
ISBN: 0-672-22235-3, $39.95

☐ Computer Dictionary (4th Edition)
Charles J. Sippl
This updated and expanded version of one of SAMS' most popular references. This dictionary of basic computer terms and handbook of computer-related topics, includes fiber optics, sensors and vision systems, computer-aided design, engineering, and

manufacturing. Clarifies micro, mini, and mainframe terminology. The 1,000 new entries in this edition focus on the RAF classifications: robotics, artificial intelligence, and factory automation. A must for every library.
ISBN: 0-672-22205-1, $24.95

☐ Artificial Intelligence Programming on the Macintosh™   *Dan Shafer, The Waite Group*
Includes tutorials in Logo as well as in Lisp and Prolog, the three main AI languages. For programmers whose background is in BASIC, an appendix shows how to convert the program examples to that language.
ISBN: 0-672-22447-X, $24.95

☐ The Best Book of: dBASE II®/III®
Ken Knecht
Written in an enjoyable, conversational style, this book describes how to detect and correct errors, sort files, create new and useful programs, and manipulate data. A time-saving guide for getting the most out of dBASE II and dBASE III and applying these systems to specific business needs.
ISBN: 0-672-22349-X, $19.95

☐ The Best Book of: Framework™
Alan Simpson
Practical examples and applications help you get the most from Framework's frames, word processor, spreadsheet, and other features. Learn how to access national information systems; how to interface with WordStar®, dBASE II®/III®, and Lotus™ 1-2-3™; how to use Framework macros; and how to program with FRED™, Framework's programming language.
ISBN: 0-672-22421-6, $17.95

☐ The Best Book of: Lotus™ 1-2-3™
Alan Simpson
This handy reference manual guides you in building spreadsheets, creating graphs, managing your database, and more. Includes practical examples and an appendix on installing Lotus 1-2-3.
ISBN: 0-672-22307-4, $14.95

☐ The Best Book of: Multiplan™
Alan Simpson
The Best Book of: Multiplan provides tips, tricks, and secrets which enable you to design more efficient and useful models. Learn to create, format, edit, and print spreadsheets, and much more.
ISBN: 0-672-22336-8, $12.95